C000076112

Building and Engineering Contracts

Building and Engineering Contracts

Law and Practice

Robert Ribeiro MA, LLM, PhD

Mitchell · *London*

© Robert Ribeiro 1990
First published 1990

All rights reserved. No part of this publication
may be reproduced, in any form or by any means,
without permission from the Publisher

Typeset by Latimer Trend & Company Ltd, Plymouth
and printed in Great Britain by
Courier International, Tiptree, Essex

Published by The Mitchell Publishing Company Limited
4 Fitzhardinge Street, London W1H 0AH
A subsidiary of BT Batsford Limited

A CIP catalogue record for this book is
available from the British Library

ISBN 0 7134 5918 2

Contents

Acknowledgment

This work would not have been possible without the help and encouragement of all those with whom I have been associated over a long period of time. In particular I would like to thank Anthony Skinner, Martin Black, Tony Swash, Peter Woodham, Reginald Balch, Mike Hanrahan, Ken Richardson, Musa Mazzawi, Margaret Wilkie, Stuart Marks, Hugo Groves, Leo D'Arcy, Patricia Sherlock and all the staff of the Law Library of PCL, and Anthony Seward and Thelma Nye of Batsford. I would also like to thank the management of the many companies which have given me access to sites, factories, facilities and equipment, contract documents, and in some instances to unreported cases which have been invaluable in compiling this book. Most of all I would like to thank my wife, Aileen Ribeiro, for her unfailing advice and assistance, and invaluable suggestions during the course of writing this work.

London 1990   RR

Preface

If, as was said in another context altogether, 'all art is quite useless', then this work is unashamedly not a work of art, since its sole justification is that it may be found useful by the readership for whom it is intended: sales and purchasing managers, project managers, project engineers, contract managers, estimators, company secretaries, business consultants, and of course students of commercial law or building or engineering. From time to time, I have been told that a work which will supply such a readership with a single and simple source of information needed for the negotiation and understanding of contracts at all points of a vast spectrum of building and engineering and commerce is not easy to find. It is hoped that if this is the case, then this work will make some advances towards filling this gap, without becoming so large as to be unwieldy or so legalistic as to be incapable of giving the practical guidance which industry requires on a day to day basis. For those who require further and more detailed reading on particular aspects of this subject, a list of works which may be consulted is given in the select bibliography. Several of these titles are the major works in their specialised areas, and to the scholarship of their authors, as well as to that of the many judges of the cases that are cited in this work, a debt is owed by all who take an interest in this perennially fascinating field.

London 1990   **RR**

1   The Making of the Contract

This work is about contracts and their uses in commercial transactions, including in particular building and engineering projects.

The expression 'contract' may mean a number of different things to different people. To a lawyer it means an agreement, promise or undertaking which is legally binding. A lawyer will tend to examine the structure of a contract to inquire whether or not it is enforceable: thus he will look for the offer made by one party and accepted by the other. He will also look at the capacity of the parties, the legality of the undertaking, the intention of the parties to create legal relations, and the existence of consideration to support a promise made by one party to another.

But to a person in business, a contract may mean something rather different: it is an instrument of commercial planning, a document or series of documents which makes arrangements for important and often complicated commercial matters such as delivery of materials, testing and approval of equipment, certification and payment, dealings with sub-contractors and suppliers, and industrial and intellectual property rights. To those in business, or engaged in building or engineering projects, the form of a contract is perhaps subordinate to its commercial or business purposes. However, the two points of view are in fact complementary. In business transactions it is essential for the proper arrangement and carrying out of the matters in hand that there should be clear and binding terms which define the respective rights and duties of the parties. Lawyers should never lose sight of the commercial ends which contracts exist to serve; equally, those in business should always keep in mind the extent to which legal matters may affect the protection they have under their contracts, or the eventual profitability of their transactions.

There is perhaps no better modern illustration of the relationship between the legal refinements of negotiating and forming a contract, and its commercial effectiveness, than the case of *British Steel Corporation* v *Cleveland Bridge and Engineering Co Ltd* (1981, reported in 1984). In this case, British Steel Corporation (BSC) successfully tendered for the production of cast-steel nodes which were to be used by Cleveland Bridge and Engineering Co Ltd (CBE) in a building project. The project required 137 cast-steel nodes for the centre of a steel frame for a bank in Saudi Arabia. The nodes required were of a unique specification, and CBE, perhaps foreseeing difficulties in delivery, sent to BSC a letter of intent requesting BSC to 'proceed immediately with the works pending the preparation and issuing to you of the official form of sub-contract'. BSC processed this order, and began preparations on the work. The conditions had not yet been agreed, and, in particular, a formal quotation had not yet been submitted, the tender price being merely an estimate based on incomplete information. The conditions put forward by CBE provided for unlimited liability for consequential loss arising from late delivery. These conditions were unacceptable to BSC. However, throughout the period of negotiations, production went ahead, and in the event BSC delivered all but one of the 137 nodes, the last being held back to ensure that payment would be made. This last node was then trapped in a steel strike, with the result that delivery of it was held up for several months in the early part of 1980. When BSC submitted its claim for the price of the goods delivered, it found that CBE had submitted to it a claim for damages for late delivery which far surpassed the claim for the price. The claim by BSC was for £229,832.70. The counterclaim by CBE was for £666,882.68, a sum which took into account the set-off between the price owed to BSC and the alleged liability of BSC for damages for delay.

In the Commercial Court, Mr Justice ROBERT GOFF held that there was *no contract* in this instance. The order by CBE was a letter of intent, but did not amount to a contract. As the judge stated, 'The real difficulty is to be found in the factual matrix of the transaction, and in particular the fact that work was being done *pending* a formal sub-contract the terms of which were still in a state of negotiation'. Having made this finding, the judge then held that there could be no obligation to deliver within any particular time without a contract, and thus there could be no liability on the part of BSC for delay. However, there *was* a liability on the part of CBE to pay a reasonable price for the goods which had been delivered to them pursuant to their request. This obligation did not arise under a contract, but under the law of 'quasi-contract' or 'restitution'. This sum was agreed by the parties during the course of the hearing to be the amount claimed by BSC, and BSC was awarded this sum.

Clearly the commercial as well as the legal uncertainties of this form of transaction are most undesirable, particularly from a purchaser's point of view. Yet it is a fact that vast sums are frequently committed to projects which take shape in a not dissimilar fashion. The important thing is that the parties should not lose sight of the need to bring the negotiations to a satisfactory conclusion, and to create legally binding contracts. For it is the contract that brings the required element of definition and certainty into the business operation. For example, a contract may specify an item of equipment or a structure which is required. This specification may be simple or relatively complex. Services may be included in the specification. The specification may also include performance data and data relating to the conditions under which the equipment is intended to operate. It is then necessary to link this specification to **conditions of contract**, which define the terms of delivery or of completion, the price or schedule of prices, and the terms about payment. These are the bare minimum of contractual terms which must be clarified. In practice, the conditions of a commercial contract will be a good deal more comprehensive than this, and will include details about what is deemed to be included in the price, about price fluctuation, if any, about changes or variations and their effect upon matters of price and delivery, about risk, insurance, title to goods, about safety and working practices, and about liabilities and warranties. This short list is not in any way comprehensive, but is only intended to give an indication at this early stage of the promises and undertakings which will be included in many contracts, and which the parties will agree to abide by. Ideally, in a good commercial contract, nothing in the negotiations is left to chance: the negotiations are carefully handled. In a major project the negotiations might take place as follows:

(a) Documents may be sent out inviting tenders or 'proposals' from prospective contractors on the basis of a specification and conditions of tender prepared by the purchaser. The documents may make it clear exactly what information is required from those submitting tenders, and may indicate certain conditions that are to be met if the tender is to be considered as 'compliant'. A special tender form may be supplied.

(b) The prospective contractors may then submit their tenders on the forms required, and on the basis of the conditions and specification proposed by the purchaser. Some tenders may be rejected as being non-compliant, ie as not conforming to the requirements of the purchaser. Others will be considered, and, depending upon the particular criteria for selection, one may be chosen. It is possible that a letter of intent may be sent out at this stage, although it must be borne in mind, following the *British Steel Corporation* v *Cleveland Bridge and Engineering Co Ltd* case, that the letter of intent may not necessarily be of any binding effect. As Mr Justice ROBERT GOFF stated in that case: 'There can be no hard and fast answer to the question whether a letter of intent will give rise to a binding agreement: everything must depend on the circumstances of the particular case'. It is therefore advisable for parties sending letters of intent to state their intentions clearly, and if a commitment to any payment for work done pursuant to a letter of intent is required, this should also be obtained in writing at this stage.

(c) Following the previous stage, a contract may be agreed by both parties. It is normal, in projects of any significant size, that this contract should be a written document signed by both parties or their representatives. There is, however, no law that such a contract needs to be signed, or even to be in a document at all. However, assuming that the contract is made by signature of a **contract document**, this document should form part of or refer to the **conditions of contract**, and the conditions of contract should refer to the **specification** and to **any other contract documents**. This may be achieved by a specific clause defining the scope of the contract, and containing the appropriate cross-references. The conditions of contract may also state the order of precedence of all the relevant documents, in case of any conflict.

The exact details and documentation and method of negotiating and forming a contract will vary from case to case. But if these important matters are handled correctly, the parties concerned will have a precise record of what they have agreed and accepted. Not every contract, by any means, is formed in this way, because business requirements vary a great deal depending upon the subject matter. In many instances, concerning for example the purchase of materials or minor services, such meticulous care in the negotiations and documentation will not be possible. Nor does the law in fact require it. In fact the law accepts a surprising degree of informality in the formation of contracts. The **legal** requirements of a contract may be simply stated, but it must always be remembered that it is a matter of commercial judgment as to what degree of care and formality is to be employed in the making of a contract, subject only to the requirement that a *few* kinds of contract, which will be described in the pages that follow, must be made or evidenced in writing.

The legal requirements of contracts

A contract requires an **offer** (eg a tender, quotation, purchase order, etc) to be made by one of the parties, and to be **accepted** by the other party. The acceptance must be before the offer lapses, or before it is withdrawn. The parties must have the **capacity** to contract, and the objects of the contract must be **legal**. The parties must, as has already been seen, conduct their negotiations in such a way as to be shown to have the **intention to create legal relations**. A qualified offer or acceptance, using words which clearly show that the essential matters have yet to be agreed, may negative intention to create legal relations at that stage, although the parties may intend to create legal relations at a later stage. If the contract is a *simple* contract (and the majority of contracts fall into this category), a further requirement is that each party must provide **consideration** for the promise by the other. This means that a party must furnish some *value* to the other party. This value may be a payment or act or form of concession or forbearance. The value need not be equal on either side, so a contract to sell a new motor car for £10 will satisfy the requirement of consideration. In summary, the legal requirements of a simple contract are usually:

offer
acceptance
capacity
legality
intention to create legal relations
consideration.

Additionally, some contracts may require **formality**. This applies in only a very few instances in English law, although the laws of other countries may differ. Contracts for sale or other disposition of land or an interest in land must be evidenced in writing to be valid. Contracts of guarantee have similar requirements. Contracts of marine insurance, and of regulated consumer credit must be in writing. But most commercial contracts for the sale of goods, or for the supply of services or of labour and materials do not require formality. In practice a degree of formality is observed because business concerns do not wish to commit large resources without written evidence of what they have agreed to. But the law does not impose any such requirement, and there are many instances of considerable liabilities being undertaken on the strength of *Telex* messages, or even oral contracts. One important instance, however, of formality being required in commercial contracts, is if the parties wish to make a contract **under seal**.

A contract made under seal, or contract made by deed, as it is sometimes called, must be contrated with a simple contract. A contract under seal is a contract which by definition requires formality, since its validity **depends upon its form**, and not upon the consideration given by one party to another. It is therefore valid without the need for consideration. On the other hand, it is not valid unless the necessary formalities have been carried out, and, in such a case, it would then be necessary for the parties to it to prove that the necessary elements of a simple contract were present, in order to enforce it. The formalities are that the contract must be in writing, sealed and delivered. A seal is either of wax or of special paper affixed to the document, or a special impression on the document. Individuals must also sign the document, whereas for a company, its seal is sufficient. Apart from the fact that such a contract needs no consideration to be enforceable, the most important point about a contract under seal is that the period within which it is possible to enforce rights under the contract is twelve years, whereas rights under simple contracts are in general barred after the lapse of six years. Contracts for building and engineering works may be made under seal, and in the case of certain types of authority or corporation this is frequently the method of contracting used. But the majority of commercial contracts will be simple contracts, made with varying degrees of formality, depending upon what the parties think is appropriate to their requirements. Major standard forms of contract drafted by bodies such as the Joint Contracts Tribunal (JCT) will contain provisions for contracts to be made under seal, but this is not to say that such methods will always be used. There have been many instances where companies, particularly those *purchasing* goods or work and materials, or services, would have been better protected had they made the contracts in question under seal. On the other hand one would not expect businesses to make the bulk of everyday transactions by this method, and it is inevitable that contracts for materials or stores or components, or for minor works, are made by less formal methods.

Example of form of words used for execution of a contract under seal

Signed, sealed and delivered by .... in the presence of......................... (*status*)........................	This form of words to be used if the contract is executed under seal by an individual or firm or unincorporated body
The common seal of .... was hereunto affixed in the presence of.................................. (*status*)........................	This form of words to be used if the contract is executed under seal by a company or by any other body corporate

Simple contracts: evaluating different types of communication

The communications which take place in ordinary business transactions, particularly in day to day transactions as opposed to major projects, often present practical difficulties. It is not always clear what a document which is written with language reflecting the business practice of a particular sector of industry actually means *in legal terms*, when we try to relate it to the requirements of a contract. Lawyers tend to speak of 'offer and acceptance', whereas in a business transaction we may have communications which take the following pattern:

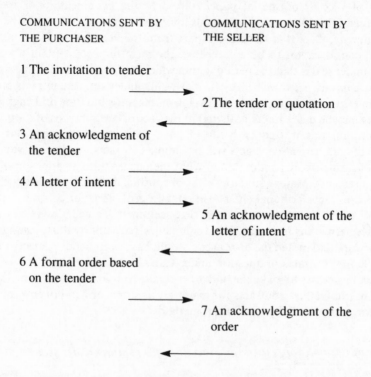

COMMUNICATIONS SENT BY THE PURCHASER	COMMUNICATIONS SENT BY THE SELLER
1 The invitation to tender	
	2 The tender or quotation
3 An acknowledgment of the tender	
4 A letter of intent	
	5 An acknowledgment of the letter of intent
6 A formal order based on the tender	
	7 An acknowledgment of the order

If the parties are in agreement about a particular set of conditions applicable to the contract, following the exchange of communications in the example given, there is no reason why any legal problem should arise (other than as to the interpretation of any of the conditions). However, one of the problems which frequently arises is that different communications may state different things or may refer to different conditions. In cases of conflict between terms and conditions or between different specifications or other requirements, it is important to know (a) whether or not a contract has actually been agreed at all, and (b) if it *has* been made, *which* communications form the contract.

It is useful, in formulating an analysis of the negotiations, to keep in mind some basic categories into which communications may fall.

1 The giving of information: the mere giving by one party of information to the other does not constitute an offer or acceptance. Thus a catalogue or price list is not in itself an offer. Nor is a factual answer to a question about, for example, one particular type of goods, or the delivery periods that are normally applicable to orders.

2 Invitations to treat: these may be made by either party, an example being the inviting of tenders. When a purchaser invites tenders, this is neither an offer nor an acceptance. The first offer will be in a tender made to the purchaser. Sellers of goods or services may also make invitations to treat: the display of goods in a shop window is an invitation to treat, since it invites customers to make offers to the shopkeeper.

3 Offers: the best definition of an offer is a communication to another party which is intended to constitute an offer, and which is capable of being accepted. In commercial contracts, the most common types of offer are *tenders* and *quotations*, which are made by prospective sellers or contractors, and *purchase* orders, which of course are made by prospective customers. Where a purchase order is made without a preceding tender or quotation, it is an offer made to the seller. Where the purchase order accepts unconditionally the offer made in a tender or quotation, it is an *acceptance*, and not an offer.

It is possible for some types of quotation to be worded in such a way as *not* to constitute an offer. The same is true of *estimates*. Much depends upon how they, or any conditions governing them, are written. In *Crowshaw* v *Pritchard and Renwick* (1899), the court held that an estimate *could* amount to an offer, and that there was no custom that an estimate was not to be an offer. Although this is an old example, it should still be treated as a warning that one should always make one's intentions clear by the wording of one's documents.

4 Acceptance: to form a contract an offer must be accepted. The acceptance must be *unconditional*, that is to say that it must not in any way alter the terms of the offer. If it does so, it will not constitute an acceptance, but will be construed as a rejection of the offer, and as the making of a 'counter-offer'. A further analysis of the position where a counter-offer is made will follow later in this chapter.

Acceptance must be in the manner indicated in the offer, but if no special method of acceptance is indicated or reasonably to be inferred, then acceptance may take place by any form of communication, including writing, *Telex*, telephone, or even conduct. Silence or inaction does *not* amount to acceptance. But care is needed here since there are occasions where a party may be silent but his *conduct* may amount to a communication of his acceptance to the other party. This would probably occur, for example, where a person who has received an offer of goods on particular terms *does not* object to those terms, and *does* willingly accept delivery of the goods. Such a situation occurred in the case of *Re Bond Worth* (1979) in which Bond Worth Ltd had ordered goods from Monsanto Ltd, and had received acknowledgment from Monsanto Ltd on a series of printed confirmation notes which were accompanied by the conditions of sale of Monsanto Ltd. Bond Worth Ltd did not take any objection to the conditions of sale of Monsanto Ltd (even though they were different from the conditions of purchase which had originally been put forward by Bond

Worth Ltd), and in fact the Company Secretary of Bond Worth Ltd acknowledged on one particular occasion that Bond Worth Ltd had received notice of a change in the conditions of sale of Monsanto Ltd. Goods were delivered on various occasions, and when a legal dispute arose, Mr Justice SLADE, in the Chancery Division of the High Court, held that each of the 29 contracts between the parties had been concluded when, but not before, the goods were delivered to and accepted by Bond Worth Ltd. 'Each of such contracts,' he stated, 'was concluded partly in writing and partly by conduct of the parties.' Normally, of course, an acceptance of an *offer* takes place well before the acceptance of the *goods*. But in cases such as Bond Worth, the acceptance of the goods is *part of* the conduct amounting to the acceptance of the offer, and the party accepting is bound by those terms which have been fairly and reasonably brought to his attention.

The timing of the acceptance

This can sometimes be of practical importance, since the rule is that an acceptance must, if it is to be valid, be made while the offer still stands. An offer stands until it lapses or until it is revoked (withdrawn). Offers may lapse either due to the expiry of a fixed period of time, or due to lapse of a reasonable period of time. Even if an offer is stated to be open for a certain period, that offer may be withdrawn at any time before it is accepted. To revoke or withdraw an offer, notice of revocation must be communicated to the person who has received the offer. A problem may occur if parties to such communications wish to know when and how their communications take effect.

The rules given below are the rules in English law. They are not necessarily the law in other countries, so special care is needed for international communications or foreign contracts.

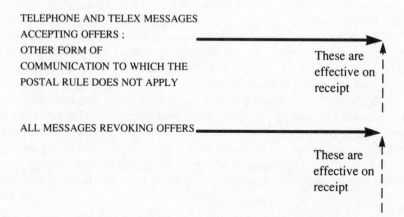

LETTERS ACCEPTING OFFERS

These are effective on dispatch, if sent by post. This rule applies where acceptance by post is expressly or impliedly permitted. Otherwise the rules are as stated below

TELEPHONE AND TELEX MESSAGES ACCEPTING OFFERS ; OTHER FORM OF COMMUNICATION TO WHICH THE POSTAL RULE DOES NOT APPLY

These are effective on receipt

ALL MESSAGES REVOKING OFFERS

These are effective on receipt

Different countries in the world follow different laws: in some, acceptance *and* revocation are only effective on *receipt*. In others, both are effective on *dispatch*. In the USA, different states follow different rules, some conforming to English law on this issue, others going their own way.

In England, the law governing acceptance by *Telex* was confirmed by the House of Lords in the case of *Brinkibon Ltd* v *Stahag Stahl und Stahlwarenhandels GmbH* (1982). In this case Brinkibon Ltd brought an action in the English courts for breach of contract by the sellers, an Austrian company in Vienna. In order to sue in England, the buyers not only had to prove that there was a contract, but also that it was *made* in England. This was because of the technical difficulty that they were seeking to serve a writ on a company which was outside the jurisdiction. The contract was for the supply of a quantity of mild steel bars. Negotiations had begun in April 1979. There were *Telex* messages from buyer to seller about the conditions of contract on 20 and 23 April.

The Seller replied on 25 April 1979.

The Buyer replied on 26 April 1979, and by this time the parties were nearing agreement on terms about weight, price, C & F terms of shipment, payment by letter of credit, and a performance bond,

The Seller then sent a *Telex* on 3 May 1979, introducing new terms about freight charges, and proposing a performance bond of 3% of the price, as compared with 5% originally proposed.

The Buyer agreed to this by *Telex* on 4 May 1979.

Thereafter, the Seller sent more *Telex* messages suggesting that the arrangements were unworkable. The contract was not performed.

Had the House of Lords concluded that there was a contract made in England, it would have been able to decide upon the merits of this dispute, and award judgment. As it was, the court held that although under English law the effect of the series of communications was that there was a contract, the contract had been made *in Austria*, and thus the dispute and alleged breach of contract would have to be tried in Austria. *Telex* messages are valid on receipt.

Offer and counter-offer

A contract is said, as a principle of law, to come into being as soon as an offer made by one party is unconditionally accepted by the other. The terms are then the terms of the offer. However, such unconditional acceptance does not always take place, particularly in commercial contracts, and it is common for the party receiving the offer, in the form of a tender or quotation or offer to purchase, to reply putting forward different terms. This may be deliberate, as for example in the *Brinkibon* case above, or it may be unintentional, as for example when a supplier intends to accept an order placed by the buyer, but in fact does so on his own form of acceptance, which refers to the supplier's own conditions of sale. The effect of an 'acceptance' which is different to the terms of the offer is that it is not truly an acceptance, but is instead a *counter-offer*. This counter-offer must in turn be accepted by the party receiving it if there is to be a contract. Furthermore, the counter-offer has the effect of 'killing' the original offer, in the sense that the original offer no longer stands, unless it is later renewed. This was held to be the law in the major engineering case of *Trollope and Colls Ltd* and *Holland and Hannen and Cubitts Ltd*, trading as *Nuclear Civil Constructors* (a firm) v *Atomic Power Constructions Ltd* (1962). In this case the problem concerned the basis of payment for work done while the details of a project were still being negotiated. T was to be a sub-contractor for the civil engineering part of the construction of a nuclear power station which the main contractor APC was to provide for the Central Electricity Generating Board. The price in the tender was approximately £9 million.

In February 1959 the parties began a long series of discussions about the terms and conditions of contract, and the specification.

In June 1959 work began on the project on the basis of a letter of intent.

In April 1960 a form of conditions was agreed upon, and a contract was made.

The question was as to the terms and conditions which were to govern the work done between June 1959 and April 1960, and the basis of payment for that work. Several possible solutions could have applied, depending upon the precise basis upon which the work between June 1959 and April 1960 was agreed as having been undertaken: it would, for example, if the parties had so wished, have been perfectly possible to have had two separate contracts governing the two periods. However, the court held that in fact *no contract* existed until April 1960. This was because of the laws of offer and counter-offer: each time a counter-offer was put forward during the course of the negotiations, it killed the original offer, so that no contract existed until a mutually acceptable offer had been made and finally accepted in April 1960. Until that date either party could have discontinued the negotiations. The court then held that the basis of payment for the work done between June 1959 and April 1960 was to be found by applying the contract retrospectively. This is not invariably the rule, but the judge held that in this case it was correct to apply this principle, as it was in conformity with the presumed intentions of the parties.

Many standard forms of condition of contract will contain a clause attempting to resolve the problem of conflicting conditions. An example is a clause stating: 'In the case of any conflict between these conditions and those of purchaser, these conditions will prevail', or 'All contracts will be deemed to be subject to our standard conditions of purchase'.

There is no harm in one party stating his intentions in this way, so long as *all* the staff of that party who are concerned with making contracts are aware that these clauses do *not* eliminate the possibility of contracts being deemed to be on other terms. The case of *Butler Machine Tool Company Ltd* v *Ex-Cell-O Ltd* (1978), is highly instructive:

On 23 May 1969, in response to an enquiry by the buyers (Ex-Cell-O) the sellers (Butler Machine Tool Company) made a quotation offering to sell a machine tool to the buyers for £75,535, delivery to be in ten months' time. The offer was stated to be subject to certain terms and conditions which 'shall prevail over any terms and conditions in the buyer's order'. The conditions included a price variation clause providing for the goods to be charged at the price ruling on the date of delivery. On 27 May the buyers replied by placing an order for the machine. The order was stated to be subject to certain terms and conditions, which were materially different from those put forward by the sellers and which, in particular, made no provision for a variation in price. At the foot of the buyers' order there was a tear-off acknowledgment of receipt of the order stating that 'We accept your order on the Terms and Conditions stated thereon'. On 5 June the sellers completed and signed the acknowledgment and returned it to the buyers with a letter stating that the buyers' order was being entered in accordance with the sellers' quotation of 23 May. When the sellers came to deliver the machine they claimed that the price had increased by £2,892. The buyers refused to pay the increase in price and the sellers brought an action claiming that they were entitled to increase the price under the price variation clause contained in their offer. The buyers contended that the contract had been concluded on the buyers' rather than the sellers' terms and was therefore a fixed-price contract.

The judge upheld the sellers' claim on the ground that the contract had been concluded on the basis that the sellers' terms were to prevail since they had stipulated that in the opening offer and all subsequent negotiations had been subject to that. The buyers appealed to the Court of Appeal. The following judgment was given by Lord DENNING:

'This case is a "battle of forms". The suppliers of a machine, Butler Tool Co Ltd (the sellers), on 23 May 1969 quoted a price for a machine tool of £75,535. Delivery was to be given in ten months. On the back of the quotation there were terms and conditions. One of them was a price variation clause. It provided for an increase in the price if there was an increase in the costs and so forth. The machine tool was not delivered until November 1970. By that time costs had increased so much that the sellers claimed an additional sum of £2,892 as due to them under the price variation clause.

'The buyers, Ex-Cell-O Corporation, rejected the excess charge. They relied on their own terms and conditions. They said, "We did not accept the sellers' quotation as it was. We gave an order for the self-same machine at the self-same price, but on the back of our order we had our own terms and conditions. Our terms and conditions did not contain any price variation clause".

'No doubt a contract was then concluded. But on what terms? The sellers rely on their general conditions and on their last letter which said "in accordance with our revised quotation of 23 May" (which had on the back a price variation clause). The buyers rely on the acknowledgment signed by the sellers which accepted the buyers' order "on the terms and conditions stated thereon" (which did not include a price variation clause).

'If those documents are analysed in our traditional method, the result would seem to me to be this: the quotation of 23 May 1969 was an offer by the sellers to the buyers containing the terms and conditions on the back. The order of 27 May 1969 purported to be an acceptance of that offer in that it was for the same machine at the same price, but it contained such additions

11

as to cost of installation, date of delivery and so forth, that it was in law a rejection of the offer and constituted a counter-offer.

'As MEGAW J said in *Trollope and Colls Limited* v *Atomic Power Constructions Limited*, ". . . the counter-offer kills the original offer". The letter of the sellers of 5 June 1969 was an acceptance of that counter-offer, as is shown by the acknowledgment which the sellers signed and returned to the buyers. The reference to the quotation of 23 May 1969 referred only to the price and identity of the machine.

'To go on with the facts of the case. The important thing is that the sellers did not keep the contractual date of delivery which was March/April 1970. The machine was ready about September 1970 but by that time the buyers' production schedule had to be re-arranged as they could not accept delivery until November 1970. Meanwhile the sellers had invoked the price increase clause. They sought to charge the buyers an increase due to the rise in costs between 27 May 1969 (when the order was given) and 1 April 1970 (when the machine ought to have been delivered). It came to £2,892. The buyers rejected the claim. The judge held that the sellers were entitled to the sum of £2,892 under the price variation clause. He did not apply the traditional method of analysis by way of offer and counter-offer. He said that in the quotation of 23 May 1969 "one finds the price variation clause appearing under a most emphatic heading stating that it is a term or condition that is to prevail". So he held that it did prevail.

'In the present case the judge thought that the sellers in their original quotation got their blow in first; especially by the provision that "These terms and conditions shall prevail over any terms and conditions in the Buyer's order". It was so emphatic that the price variation clause continued through all the subsequent dealings and that the buyer must be taken to have agreed to it. I can understand that point of view. But I think that the documents have to be considered as a whole. And, as a matter of construction, I think the acknowledgment of 5 June 1969 is the decisive document. It makes it clear that the contract was on the buyers' terms; and the buyers' terms did not include a price variation clause.

'I would therefore allow the appeal and enter judgment for the buyers.'

Oral and written agreements

Contracts may be made orally or partly orally. A problem occasionally arises as to what has been agreed. There is nothing to prevent parties from agreeing orally to contract on the basis of standard terms known to both sides. The terms must be capable of identification: an agreement to contract on 'usual' conditions would be too uncertain to be a contract, and would be unenforceable if the parties had not in fact agreed on all the essential terms. Exceptionally the courts might enforce such an agreement, if despite the apparent vagueness of language, the parties had in reality agreed the essential terms.

The mere counting of occasions on which the parties have *previously* contracted on a given set of terms is probably not enough in itself to justify the inference that they intended to base a new oral agreement on those same terms.

A better test is to look at all the circumstances to see what terms the parties would have had in mind when contracting orally (assuming that they do not refer to a specific set of terms).

Thus in *British Crane Hire Corporation* v *Ipswich Plant Hire Ltd* (1975), where a crane which was urgently needed was hired by telephone, the owners of the crane sent the written terms *after* the crane was delivered. By this time the crane had been accidentally damaged by sinking into a marsh, which the customer was draining. The conditions provided that the customer would bear the cost of recovery, but the customer disputed that the conditions governed the oral agreement. *The Court of Appeal* decided that the parties would have had in mind standard terms commonly used in this field, when making the oral agreement. As the owners' terms were in common use, the court held that they had been incorporated into the oral agreement by common understanding, particularly since the customer used similar terms, when letting out cranes.

However, if there is *no* common understanding between the parties as to the application of a particular form of conditions, or if the parties intend the oral agreement to stand on its own, without reference to any other conditions, then documents sent by one of the parties subsequently cannot alter the oral contract, and can at best be a record of what was agreed orally. In *Grayston Plant Ltd* v *Plean Precast Ltd* (1976) an English company hired equipment to a company in Scotland. This equipment was damaged through no fault of the parties. It is common for conditions of hire to allocate the risk and burden of insurance to one or other of the parties in these circumstances, but the contract was made orally, by telephone, and no particular terms and conditions had been referred to in the conversation. In this particular case the judge declined to hold that the conditions of hire of the owners of the equipment were part of the contract. In his view, the conditions were not familiar to people contracting in Scotland, and it could not be assumed that the customer had intended to contract on those particular terms. Of course, there is nothing to stop parties who wish to rely upon their own conditions from actually mentioning them expressly in a conversation, and then following this up with a written record of the transaction.

THE INCORPORATION OF TERMS INTO THE CONTRACT

Major contracts are or ought to be made formally, listing in order of precedence the documents that are intended to be part of the contract. This establishes clearly what the terms of the contract are, and clarifies the relationship between the terms and conditions and the technical or delivery requirements. Having said this, we must accept that a good many contracts are made less formally. Sometimes documents are not actually sent out, but are simply *referred to*. This is perfectly in order, and indeed the principle that terms and conditions can be incorporated into a contract by reference follows naturally from the principles seen in the case of *British Crane Hire Corporation* v *Ipswich Plant Hire Ltd* (1975) already discussed. The conditions of a contract are those by which the parties have agreed to be bound, and if a reference to certain conditions is sufficiently clear to both parties, and is accepted, then those will be the conditions of the contract.

Thus in *Smith* v *South Wales Switchgear Ltd* (1978), a company made a purchase order stating in writing that the order was 'subject to our General Conditions of Contract, obtainable on request'. This was held to be sufficient to incorporate the latest revision of the conditions at the time of the order into the contract. The court held that the reference made it clear how the seller was to find out what the buyer's conditions were.

On the other hand it can sometimes be a good deal less clear which documents or communications have been incorporated into the contract. Anything short of the most careful attention to these matters can leave a party to a contract in an unguarded position. The case of *Davis Contractors* v *Fareham UDC* demonstrates this. Here a contractor had intended to protect himself against a possible shortage of labour and materials. His letter to the local authority stated:

> 'Our tender is subject to adequate supplies of material and labour being available as and when required to carry out the work in the time specified.'

This letter contained a number of paragraphs, and a different part of the letter referred to the working of the 'fluctuations' clause in the contract. When the contract was finalised, it referred to the **tender**, but *not* to the **letter**. The tender, however, did refer to *part* of the letter, but only the part concerning fluctuations, and *not* to the part concerning materials and labour. The court held here that the part of the letter concerning materials and labour was not part of the contract, and thus the contractor was not legally protected against shortages of labour or materials.

Another striking example of the ways in which a business may inadvertently fail to incorporate its conditions of business into a contract was *Wavin Nederland BV* v *Excombe Ltd* (1983). In this case, Wavin delivered goods to Excombe Ltd under a contract of sale. In the general conditions of sale of Wavin was a condition stating that the property in the goods was to remain that of Wavin until payment had been made in full. However, when a dispute arose, the Commercial Court found on the evidence that the conditions of sale had not been incorporated into the contract in question. There had been *no express* incorporation of the conditions, and there was no consistency in the dealings between the parties which would give rise to the inference that the parties had intended to incorporate the conditions into the relevant contract. The court found that, looking at transactions between the parties, Wavin's approach had been unsystematic and irregular, and this was fatal to any attempt to *imply* that the conditions had been incorporated into the contract.

REPRESENTATIONS AND ADDITIONAL TERMS

There are a number of ways in which a statement made by a party to a contract, prior to the making of the contract, may have a legally binding effect. Such statements may take effect as:

(a) representations; or

    (b)   collateral contracts; or

    (c)   terms of the contract in question.

Representations   If a party to a contract, or his agent, makes a representation of fact which is intended to be relied upon by the other party, and is in fact relied upon, this statement must be true, since if it is not, the other party may have a remedy in respect of misrepresentation. This principle is of some importance in commercial contracts and in building contracts, since it is possible that commercial literature or prospectuses or specifications may misrepresent some fact, such as site conditions, or the nature of a product. It is not necessary that a representation should be made knowing it to be false: the law of misrepresentation applies to innocent misrepresentation, as well as to negligent misrepresentation and fraudulent misrepresentation. In many cases this will give to a party, whether the employer or the contractor, the right to *rescind* the contract in question. In a few cases it will give rise to damages either instead of or in addition to rescission: *Misrepresentation Act 1967*.

Collateral contracts   These are agreements or promises or warranties which are given separately from and are supplementary to the contract itself. They may be made in letters or other documents, or even orally. The existence of collateral contracts depends upon *agreement*, and it is a matter of evidence whether or not there is such agreement, or whether, conversely, the final contract document is intended to override and supersede earlier requests, discussions or negotiations. The decision in the case of *J. Evans and Son (Portsmouth) Ltd* v *Andrea Merzario Ltd* (1976), which is discussed in the following paragraph, is based partly upon the finding that a collateral warranty had been given.

Terms of the contract   It is open to a court to find, as a matter of evidence, that the contract itself has been concluded in more than one document, or partly in writing and partly orally. The distinction between a collateral contract and a term of a contract is often a rather fine one, and in most cases of no great practical importance: at the end of the day we are asking whether or not a promise or undertaking can be enforced or relied upon. The case of *J. Evans and Son (Portsmouth) Ltd* v *Merzario Ltd* (1976) shows that where a promise or undertaking is a collateral warranty, or where it is an express term of the contract, it is indeed binding. In this case, J. Evans and Son Ltd, importers of machines from Italy, had discussions with the general manager of Andrea Merzario Ltd, in London (the head office being in Italy), regarding an order for the carriage of an injection moulding machine in a container. In the course of the discussion it was agreed orally that the machine would be shipped in a container *under deck*. J. Evans and Son Ltd had insisted on this because of possible damage by sea spray. On the basis of the assurance received, J. Evans and Son Ltd agreed a contract of carriage with Andrea Merzario Ltd.

    By an oversight the container was shipped on deck. It fell overboard and was lost. J. Evans and Son Ltd claimed damages against Andrea Merzario Ltd for the loss of the machine, alleging that there had been a breach of contract. Andrea Merzario Ltd relied upon its written standard terms of carriage, which at first sight appeared to give it complete freedom to decide how the goods were to be shipped, and which purported to limit its liability. The Court of Appeal held that J. Evans and Son Ltd was entitled to damages for breach of contract. The court held that the assurance given by Andrea Merzario Ltd was binding either as a collateral warranty, or as an express term of the contract which had been made partly orally, partly in writing, and partly by conduct. The oral promise that the goods would be shipped under deck was to be treated as overriding the printed conditions, since the court was entitled to look at all the evidence to decide what bargain had been struck by the parties.

The role of fairness in the construction of a contract

In all the cases cited so far in which a court has decided what were the terms of a particular contract, there has always been one factor in common: the decision has always been based upon what a party to a contract can be taken to have agreed, and what can be said to have been fairly and reasonably brought to his attention at the time when he accepted the offer. After the *Bond Worth* case had made it clear that offers can be accepted by conduct, such as by taking delivery of the goods, there remained the practical question of how far a seller, supplier or contractor had to go in bringing the terms to the attention of the buyer. Could the terms and conditions simply be contained in a *delivery note*, so that the buyer could be said to have accepted the terms and conditions on receipt of the goods? This question has now, to some extent, been resolved by the Court of Appeal, which has made it clear that such a method of contracting will *not* be effective to impose onerous or unusual terms and conditions upon a buyer. In the case of *Interfoto Ltd* v *Stiletto Ltd* (1988) a bag of transparencies was delivered with a delivery note which contained the word CONDITIONS in capitals. It then set out the conditions, one of which imposed a charge of £5 per day for each transparency retained beyond a 14 day period. The court held that this condition had not been accepted by the customer, and was not part of the contract. When a condition was particularly onerous or unusual, and would not usually be known to the other party, the party seeking to enforce it had to show that it had fairly and reasonably been brought to the attention of the other party. The words of Lord Justice BINGHAM are worth repeating:

'In many civil law systems and perhaps in most legal systems outside the common law world, the law of obligations recognises and enforces an overriding principle that in making and carrying out contracts parties should act in good faith ... its effect is most aptly conveyed by such metaphorical colloquialisms as "playing fair", "coming clean" or "putting one's cards face upwards on the table". It is in essence a principle of fair and open dealing.'

It should be noted that this case *does* appear to decide that it is possible for a seller to impose terms upon the buyer by bringing those terms to the notice of the buyer as part of the offer. In this particular case the court decided that there was no evidence that the parties had reached agreement over the telephone (presumably because at that stage the subject matter of the contract had not been sufficiently identified, and the parties did not intend to make a firm contract). Thus the telephone conversation amounted to a mere preliminary inquiry, and did not amount to a contract. The contract was concluded when the goods arrived, and were accepted by the customer (who in this case was a hirer rather than a buyer). The dispatch of the goods, together with the terms of the contract, was the offer; the acceptance of the goods was the thing that brought into existence the contract. But the terms of the offer *only* became part of the contract *if* they had been fairly and reasonably brought to the attention of the customer.

ENTIRE AGREEMENT

As may be seen from the foregoing pages, the construction of a contract may be a complex issue. But if businesses are to avoid costly and damaging disputes, it is essential for them to be able to identify *all* the terms and conditions and other details of the contracts which they have entered into. One way of achieving this, particularly in larger contracts which are individually negotiated, is to make it clear in the written contract that the contract between the parties represents the *entire agreement* between the parties. A clause which states this, and which makes it clear that the contract supersedes and replaces all previous negotiations, whether oral or written, and which also states that no represen-tations or collateral agreements exist between the parties or have been relied upon between the parties, will be treated as very strong evidence that the written contract which the parties then sign *is* the contract, and the entire contract, between the parties. In order to go outside the terms of such a written contract, the most *stringent proof* would be required on the part of the party wishing to do so, and in most cases this would not be possible. Thus the reduction of negotiations to a definite, fully comprehensive, written contract, signed by the parties, and containing an 'entire agreement' clause, is one way of bringing a degree of certainty to complex issues.

2 Price and Payment

The contract should contain or refer to a price or series of prices, or to a definite method of calculating a price (for example by reference to the market price of gold on a specified exchange on a specified date). A price does not have to be a definite figure. What is important is that the required element of certainty should be brought into the contract. If an agreement is made and there is only a vague or indeterminate method of deciding what is the price, this is not only commercially disadvantageous, but it may also show that the parties have not in fact made a contract at all.

In *Courtney and Fairbairn Ltd* v *Tolaini Bros* (1975), it was held by the Court of Appeal that an agreement to 'negotiate fair and reasonable contract sums . . . based upon agreed estimates of the net cost of the work and general overheads with a margin for profit of 5%' did not amount to a binding and enforceable contract. The estimates mentioned had not yet been agreed, but were still to be agreed. Lord DENNING stated:

> 'Now the price in a building contract is of fundamental importance. It is so essential a term that there is no contract unless the price is agreed or there is an agreed method of ascertaining it, not dependent on the negotiations of the two parties themselves.'

In short, it is not the absence of a stated price that is fatal to the existence of a contract: it is the absence of a definite and non-negotiable method of ascertaining the price. If during the negotiations, the parties fail to agree the price or the basis for ascertaining the price, there is no contract. However, if the parties each put forward different proposals as to the price, as happened in *Butler Machine Tool Ltd* v *Ex-Cell-O Ltd* (1978), there will be a contract if one party accepts the other's proposal along with the other terms offered.

Where there is no price, and no contract, there may yet be a duty to pay. If work is done, or goods supplied, without a contract, and if the work has been done, or the goods supplied pursuant to a request or instruction to proceed by the other party, there will be a duty to pay a reasonable sum for the work or goods. This is not a contractual payment, but a payment under the law of 'quasi-contract', or the law of restitution. It is sometimes known as a *quantum meruit*. In the case of *British Steel Corporation* v *Cleveland Bridge Engineering Co Ltd* (1981), this was the nature of the payment which was eventually awarded to BSC, when it was held that no contract existed. It was also the nature of the sum which was sought, unsuccessfully, by the sub-contractor in *Trollope and Colls Ltd* v *Atomic Power Constructions Ltd* (1962). In this case the court held that a contract had eventually come into existence, and that its terms as to price and payment governed all work done, including work done before the contract was agreed. It is perhaps fortunate for industry that this was the conclusion reached by the court, since so much work is in fact done in advance of contracts being agreed, and without the ability to apply contractual provisions retrospectively it would be almost impossible to bring any discipline into the pricing of such work. Furthermore, although a seller or contractor may derive some advantage from a quantum meruit claim for a reasonable sum for work done or for goods supplied, a buyer will require the existence of a contract if he is to be able to make a claim for the enforcement of specific rights or duties, such as delivery of the goods within a given time. Even sellers or contractors should be aware that to undertake work under an instruction of the other party, without a contract, is to run the risk that the order may be cancelled at any time, since there is no contract.

Methods of pricing

Prices may be formulated as lump sums, or they may include a fee and the actual costs of all the items supplied or of sub-contracted work. They may be stated by reference to known quantities of goods or materials, or they may refer to items to be measured at a later stage. It is not uncommon for tenders to be made on alternative terms at alternative prices. If this happens it is of course essential that there should be *clarity* as to the tender which has been accepted. In the case of *Peter Lind and Co Ltd* v *Mersey Docks and Harbour Board* (1972), alternative tenders had been submitted, one on a 'fixed-price' basis, and one on a 'cost-plus' basis. The employers purported to accept 'your tender'. It was not at all clear which tender had been accepted, so there was *no contract*. The work done had to be paid for on a quantum meruit basis, ie on the basis that as there was no contract stating the price of the work, the basis of payment would have to be that of a reasonable sum for work done.

The language of pricing

At the time of writing, one of the problems that appears to recur throughout industry and commerce is that of finding a common language in which to express a mutual understanding in relation to the price of a particular commercial transaction. The kind of question which may arise is whether or not a stated price is intended to be strictly accurate, or whether it is only intended to be an estimated price, which may alter upwards or downwards. A similar question is whether a price, once agreed in a contract, is capable to being adjusted, for example to take account of increased costs, or whether it is not. Expressions such as 'fixed price', 'firm price', 'budgetary price', and many others abound, and they are not always used in exactly the same sense. There are many forms of contract in which one or more of these expressions may have been *defined*, in the definitions clause, or elsewhere in the contract. Such definitions must always be studied with care.

As has already been stated earlier in this work, there is no rule that an estimate cannot be an offer, so by the same token, it is possible that a price described in an estimate could yet amount to a firm and binding contractual price. Those who give estimated or 'budgetary' prices, intending them to be purely for guidance, but in no way intending them to be the actual price required when the work is done, should take care to make this clear. There are a number of ways in which this can be done. Either the expressions used can be defined or the context in which they can appear can be qualified in such a way that it is not possible for the estimated or budgetary price to become binding upon the person giving it. An example of how this could be done would be where a contractor giving an *estimate* states that this is not intended to be an offer, and that no contract is to come into being until the *order* of the customer has been received and *accepted* by the contractor. This would then mean that the customer would place an order in accordance with the estimate, and when the contractor had received it, the contractor would have a chance to revise his estimated price, and if necessary to alter it. (This alteration would then have to be accepted by the customer.)

Fixed and firm prices

Prices may be agreed in a contract, but the contract may contain an agreed mechanism or formula for adjusting the price. This is a matter for negotiation before the contract is made. The general rule of law is that agreed, fixed, prices cannot be altered or adjusted after the contract has been made unless there is a provision allowing for such an adjustment. The existence of such a provision is a matter of analysis of the terms of the contract, and this was the subject of the dispute in the case of *Butler Machine Tool Ltd* v *Ex-Cell-O Ltd*, which has already been discussed. It is therefore important to resolve any conflict between the terms of the buyer and the terms of the seller on this matter.

The expression 'fixed' price is sometimes used in contrast to a 'cost-plus' type of contract. However, with this meaning of 'fixed price' it is still possible that there may be additions to or adjustments of the price, if the contract so provides. It is not a question of words having a rigid meaning, but a question of the precise details of what is set down in the contract. In order to cope with these problems, some contractors and purchasers use the expression 'firm price' or 'fixed and firm price' to mean a price which is not only fixed, but not subject to alteration either. It is in the interests of all parties that uses should become standardised throughout industry, but at present this is not the case, and care should be taken. To quote Lord Justice DONALDSON:

> 'It is a wise and elementary precaution to agree expressly upon the terms of a contract before undertaking its performance. The parties to this appeal failed to do so. The resulting controversy was wholly predictable.'
> (*Esmil Ltd* v *Fairclough Civil Engineering Ltd* (1981))

Mistakes

Those in business make mistakes at their peril, and if this results in the underpricing of a tender or other offer, there is a risk that this may be accepted so as to become a binding contract. It is possible to withdraw an offer before it is accepted, but this requires firstly that the error in pricing be picked up in time, and secondly that the notice of withdrawal of the offer be given to *and received by* the person to whom the offer is made. In many important contracts there is another factor which comes into play, which is that the offer or tender may be backed by a 'bid bond' or 'tender bond' provided by a bank or other company at the instigation of the seller. This does not prevent a tender from being withdrawn, but for practical purposes it may make it onerous.

Commercial errors or errors of judgment would be normally known only to the party making them, and would not necessarily be perceived as such by the other party. If a buyer has received a tender for work to be done for £48,000, when the other competing tenders are for the same work for £50,000, he will be entitled to assume that the difference is due to competitiveness rather than due to a mistake. If in this case the successful tenderer has priced the work at too low a price, he will not be able to rectify the contract. However, it may be that the circumstances of an offer or tender are such that the error is an obvious one, such as a figure which is only one tenth of the original one discussed, or such as an entire item or document being left out when both parties know perfectly well that it was to be included. In such cases the law will not permit one party to take an unfair advantage of the other. The resulting transaction will either be held not to be a contract at all, or else will be held to be voidable at the option of the party in error. The test will be one of what it is reasonable for the party receiving the offer to have known in the circumstances.

A mistaken assumption upon which a contractor bases his price will not normally assist the contractor in changing his price or in getting any other kind of assistance under the contract (unless the employer is willing to make a concession, and there is no legal obligation to do this). In the case of *Ibmac Ltd* v *Marshall Ltd* (1968) the contractors quoted a price for the building of a road. The quotation was accepted, and work started. The site was at the bottom of a steep hill, and the contractors had not foreseen difficulties regarding surface water. This in fact created problems which the contractors then expected the employer to put right. However, it was held that in this particular contract it was the responsibility of the contractors to complete the work at the price quoted and accepted. It was not the responsibility of the employer to put the site into a state which would make it easier or cheaper to do the work. The contractors were not entitled to payment until the work was done. It follows from this case that all those who enter into contracts should, before quoting, make a careful assessment of the site conditions and other conditions which may affect the price and timing and feasibility of the work, and take full account of them in the quotation. Many contracts have specific provisions about who is responsible for site conditions, and these should also be known and understood. Nor are site conditions the only factor concerning which there could be mistaken assumptions. Another area in which problems arise is that of *what is included* in the price. A moment's reflection will remind any person in business that prices may include, or exclude *any* of the following (which is not an exhaustive list):

the goods/materials	installation
packaging	commissioning
delivery	standard tests
loading/unloading	special tests
operating instructions	maintenance
drawings	spare parts

A good contract will therefore make it clear what is included in the price, and what is excluded, and what, if provided, will be the subject of a separate agreement, such as a maintenance agreement or spare parts agreement.

The effect of variations or changes

In a simple contract for the sale of goods the price will be based upon the prices quoted or the prices ruling for the items described in the contract, and the buyer will have no right to change the contract without entering into fresh orders or negotiations with the seller for extra or different items. In more sophisticated contracts, the contract conditions may make provision for *variations* or *changes* or *extras or additions*. Such provisions exist in virtually all standard national conditions of building and engineering contract. They entitle the employer, or his representative, such as architect or engineer, to ask for variations to the work or to the order, and provide that such variations will become binding upon the contractor, and will be governed by certain other provisions in the contract regarding price adjustment (if any) and time extension (if any).

Not every change or variation necessarily affects the contract price, but the chances are that it will, and for this reason some thought is needed as to what is the most practicable method of coping with the price adjustments following a change order or order for a variation. This will depend a great deal upon the nature of the work being done, and upon the parties and the relationship between them. It will also depend upon the *internal* procedures which have to be met in different companies, and which have been designed to make sure that the decision goes through the right hands and that a proper evaluation of the proposed variation is made. Under some contract conditions a variation will be the subject of a *quotation*, which will be sent by the contractor and negotiated with the employer. Under other contract conditions a variation will be the subject of an *instruction* by the employer or his authorised representative, and the varied work will be measured and priced subsequently. The pricing may then be governed by an agreed formula in the contract, or it may be simply governed by the criterion of fair and reasonable prices. Some contracts provide for a choice of methods of price adjustment following variations, and this is because experience has shown that while the quotation method has the most certainty, it is not the ideal way of coping with an emergency, which may require prompt action and subsequent pricing of the variation. More will be said about variations at a later stage, since they also raise important questions about **authority**, the **scope** of the contract, and **time extensions**.

Payment: entire contracts

In contracts for the sale of goods, and in building and engineering contracts, the parties are entitled to negotiate whatever arrangements they wish to make as to how and when the price shall be paid. It is desirable that there should be clarity as to the agreement made, and that the parties should understand the full legal implications of their bargain. In the case already discussed, of *Ibmac Ltd* v *Marshall Ltd*, the contractor Ibmac had claimed the value of work done after they had abandoned the work, and had been replaced as contractor. But the claim was unsuccessful because this was an 'entire' contract, that is, a contract which had to be performed entirely before the price was due. The concept of an entire contract is an important one. A contract may state that the whole of a piece of work must be performed before any of the price is due; or it may state that the whole of the price must be paid in advance before any performance is due. In each case, part performance or part payment will not suffice to activate the duty of the other party. The contract is entire. Lump sum contracts may be entire contracts, as opposed to contracts which provide for stage payments. A contract using bills, or 'measured' contract, may also be an entire contract, if the eventual sum payable is to be paid as a single sum. In the case of *Ibmac Ltd* v *Marshall Ltd*, there was some uncertainty as to whether the contract was for a fixed price or to be measured with bills of quantities. This did not affect the results, which was that the contract was an entire one, and that as it had not been performed, *none* of the price was due. (The original judge in this trial had found that the contractor was in breach, but had awarded the contractor some of the price claimed. This finding was held by the Court of Appeal to be wrong.)

A similar result occurred many years earlier in the case of *Foreman* v *The Liddlesdale* (1900), in which a ship had been damaged, and the agent of the owner had authority to contract for the damage to be repaired. The repairers did not carry out the work as specified, but did different work, which they alleged to have been done with the authority of the agent, and which they also alleged to be equivalent to or better then the required work. The repairers lost their case on all counts. The work was not authorised, and the owner had no duty to pay for it. The contract was an entire one and in its entirety had not been performed, so no payment could be claimed.

Even if a price is itemised into different sums for different items, the contract may yet be an entire one if that is its purport. However, the next question which arises is the precise *degree* of performance of an entire contract which is required if there is to be payment. Some contracts may be *strict as to performance*, and nothing short of exact completion will suffice. Other contracts may allow for *substantial performance* to be treated as sufficient performance of an entire contract. There cannot be hard and fast rules about what are obviously matters of degree, but it is thought that in a building or engineering contract, in the absence of any express provisions to the contrary, a party who has *substantially* performed the work, and who has not deliberately broken his contract, will be entitled to payment. The defects may then be put right under warranty, or there may be deductions from the price to take account of the defects.

A case which illustrates the rule about substantial performance is *Bolton* v *Mahadeva* (1972) in which a plumbing and central heating contractor contracted to design and supply a central heating system. The system was installed, but when tested it was found to have serious defects. It gave out fumes when switched on, and produced inadequate heat, due to insufficient radiators and insulation. The contractor sued the employer for the price. At the county court stage of the action, the judge awarded the contractor the amount claimed, less certain deductions for deficiencies. But on appeal, the Court of Appeal held that payment was only due when the contract had been *substantially* performed, and in this case the discrepancies were such that the work could not be said to have been substantially performed. Small deficiencies would not have disentitled the contractor to payment, but in this case the court had to take into account the nature of the defects and the proportion of the expense of rectifying them to the contract price. In fact the cost of rectifying the deficiencies would have been something in the region of one third of the contract price, in this case, and the deficiencies were such that the heat was 26% to 30% short of what was required, in some parts of the building. Clearly this fell short of substantial performance.

Because of these legal difficulties, as well as for the better protection of the contractor, modern building and engineering contracts tend to provide for *stage payments*.

Stage payments

These may be provided for in a number of possible ways. Broadly speaking, we are looking at contracts under which the price (whether a fixed price or a price to be measured), is to be paid in instalments or stages. These instalments of the price are to be paid on a particular date or on the occurrence of a particular event. These matters must be set out in the contract: there can be no implied terms as to stage payments, in normal circumstances.

Dates   It is possible to write a contract on the basis that instalments of the price are to be paid on specific dates, such as calendar dates. This may be a desirable method of arranging for payment where it is not practicable to key the payments into *events* (see paragraph below), because the events cannot be described or quantified with sufficient precision. It may, in a particular type of project, such as the building of complex plant on site, be more practicable *to measure and evaluate the work done on set dates*, and to base stage payments on each evaluation. The contractor then has greater likelihood of receiving payment regularly, while the employer has a reduced risk of overpayment, because he is only paying for what is performed at each date.

Events   Many kinds of building and engineering contract are written on the basis that payment is due when one or more *events* has occurred. Thus a typical contract for the supply and installation of equipment may provide that 20% of the price is to be paid on the making of the contract, a further 50% to be paid on delivery of the equipment, a further 25% to be paid on the commissioning or handover of the equipment, and the final 5% to be held as 'retention money' by the employer until the expiration of the defects liability or warranty period, and paid at the end of this period. (These figures and events are of course purely hypothetical, and each contract must be written according to its own individual circumstances or requirements.)

With this kind of payment provision, where payment can be said to be 'keyed in' to certain *events*, it is in the interests of the *contractor*, in particular, that it should be possible to define each event with as much accuracy and precision as can be reasonably arranged. There is nothing illegal or unfair about a contract under which work has to be carried out to the *satisfaction* of the employer or his architect or engineer. Indeed many contracts are written in precisely this way. From the employer's point of view, this is aimed, no doubt, at the objective of getting the desired result and full value for money. On the other hand this can be a problem for the contractor, who may find that some (but not necessarily all) employers will keep him waiting for his money, on the ground that the work has not been completed to the employer's satisfaction. This problem can to some extent be overcome by building as much objectivity as is possible into the specification, and by careful staging of payments.

Retention money

In commercial contracts, particularly the more important ones, it is not uncommon for the purchaser or employer to stipulate that some of the price is to be held back, and paid only when the employer is completely satisfied that the goods or buildings or plant are in good working order. This is often known as 'retention money', or even more simply as a 'retention'. This use of the word relates to sums of money, which are retained by the employer, usually as security for performance in full of all the contractor's obligations, including in particular the carrying out of work under the warranty or defects liability clause. The word 'retention' as used here must not be confused with 'retention of title', which is discussed in chapter 4, and which presents a very different issue.

Retention money can be provided for under the contract in a number of possible ways. One method is to provide a programme of stage payments, and to state that out of each amount certified as a stage payment, a certain percentage will be held by the employer as a retention. The employer thus builds up a reserve of retention money throughout the period of the contract, and this reserve always bears the same proportion to the amount paid under the contract. See diagram overleaf.

An alternative way of providing for retention money is simply to create a programme of stage payments, with each payment being payable in full at the particular stage when it arises, and to use the *final* stage as a form of retention. The last instalment will be of a relatively small percentage, and will be released at a stage described in the contract, which will normally be when the contractor has fulfilled all his obligations under the contract.

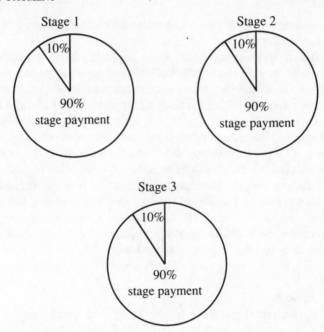

Stage 4 = release of retention money

Example

The Buyer will pay the contract price stated in this contract to the Contractor as follows:

1 ...% upon the signing of the contract.
2 ...% when the goods and materials have been delivered to the site.
3 ...% when the works have been completed in accordance with this contract and a certificate of completion has been signed by the Engineer.
4 ...% when the works have been tested and a certificate of approval of the tests has been signed by the Engineer, and the works have been handed over to the Buyer.
5 5% when the guarantee period stated in this contract has expired and it has been certified by the Engineer that all defects which have been notified to the Contractor within the guarantee period have been rectified.

Several points must be made as to retention money:
(a) The amount to be deducted as a retention is negotiable between the parties. In some contracts it may be 5%, in others 10% or 20%.
(b) There is no implied right to deduct retention money. The right exists only where there is a provision giving such a right in the contract. If the contract does not provide for retention money, then the employer may: pay in full, but insist on repairs or warranty work being carried out; *or* refuse to pay at all, on the ground that the contract is an entire one and the

26

work is either defective or not substantially performed; *or* pay for substantial performance, but make specific deductions in respect of specific deficiencies. However, these courses of action all have their disadvantages, and require great care; whereas a system of retention money may be far more convenient to operate.

(c) A contract which has stage or interim payments may yet be an *entire* one as to the retention money. By this we mean that although the interim payments may be paid for less than complete work (depending upon the way the contract is written), it may be that the release of the *retention* requires *complete performance* of the contractor's obligations. This would be a logical interpretation of many contracts, since that is the whole purpose of retention money; but it is very much a matter of interpretation of each contract. Certainly, no contractor should lightly enter into a contract in which the event upon which the payment of the retention money is due is not carefully defined.

(d) It is not enough simply to state in a contract that there is to be a retention of a certain amount or percentage of the price. The parties will also need to know how the money is to be *held* (eg whether by the employer on his own account, or by the employer as trustee for the contractor). Further, the procedures for the *release* of the retention money need to be known. Sometimes retention money is released as a single sum, and sometimes in stages. Further, the parties will need to give consideration to the question of what are to be the employer's *rights of deduction* from the retention. A model of how to consider provisions about retention money exists in JCT (1980) forms of building contract, although its provisions are perhaps unduly complex, and will not suit every party.

(e) Retention money may be dealt with in a contract as an issue on its own, or it may be dealt with in conjunction with the related issue of *performance bonds* and other bonds and guarantees. These points will be looked at in detail in chapter 10.

NON-PAYMENT: THE POSITION OF THE SELLER OR CONTRACTOR

An undertaking to pay the price or any part of it is a binding obligation if set down in the contract. As such, it must be observed, otherwise legal consequences follow. We will now examine what these legal consequences may be, and what the seller or contractor who has not received a payment which is due may do about it. It should be said that we are looking at this issue from a purely *legal* point of view. Apart from legal action or direct legal remedies, there are no doubt commercial measures which a seller or contractor may take against bad debtors, but these will not be considered here. From a different point of view, it may also be observed in passing that many sellers and contractors have to put up with a good deal from certain of their customers, as far as slow payment is concerned, but to resort to legal action in cases of this kind is not always a practicable proposition, since the seller or contractor may be dependent upon repeat orders from those very same customers. A good credit control manager may in many cases be a more effective way of dealing with these problems than resort to the law. However, there are a number of legal principles which are now about to be discussed which, if properly used, can be of help to sellers and contractors.

Points to check
1   When is payment *due*? Has that date or event occurred?
2   What *specific rights* are reserved to the seller under the contract?
3   What *common law or statutory* rights are relevant to the case in hand?

SPECIFIC PROVISIONS IN THE CONTRACT

These are negotiable by the parties, and may include **liens** both of the general and the particular type, rights to bring an **action for the price** or any part of it, rights to claim **charges** or **damages**, rights to **terminate** the contract, rights to **recover the goods**, and **rights to charge interest** on overdue sums.

Not all these remedies are necessarily relevant to a particular contract, and the precise combination that is written into the contract will depend upon what is thought by the seller to be desirable, and upon what is acceptable to the buyer.

As an example, in *George Barker (Transport) Ltd* v *Eynon* (1974), a transport contractor had contracted under the Conditions of Carriage of the Road Haulage Association, stating that the carrier was to have a general lien against the owner of any goods for any monies whatsoever due from such owner to the carrier. This *contractual lien* meant that the carrier had the right to refuse to release the goods if money was owed to it by the owner of the goods. A lien may in some cases be implied by law, but a specific provision conferring a lien may in many cases be more valuable, partly to establish its priority over other creditors of the owner of the goods, and partly because it may be stated to be a *general lien* (ie a lien over any goods in relation to any money outstanding), as compared with a lien only over particular goods in relation to particular money.

By common law and under statute, certain persons have a lien over goods, that is, the right to withhold delivery of those goods. Under the Sale of Goods Act 1979, the unpaid seller of goods has a lien over them until the price has been paid. This does not apply where the seller has given credit to the buyer unless the credit has expired or the buyer has become insolvent. These rights which exist by statute can be improved upon (from the point of view of the seller) by specific terms of the contract. By definition, a lien means the right to withhold deliveries in certain circumstances. It merely means holding back the goods, and not termination of the contract or re-selling the goods to another party. However, the contract may contain specific terms about re-sale of the goods in certain circumstances, or about the right of the unpaid seller to terminate the contract. Even if these specific terms did not exist, there would be a point at which under common law the buyer would be *deemed* to have *repudiated* his obligations under the contract, by not paying, and at which the seller would be entitled to bring the contract to an end and to sell the goods to another person. However, at common law this point is not always easy to define, and re-sale of the goods, after the exercise of a seller's lien, requires notice to the buyer, except in the case of perishables.

A case which shows the value of specific provisions in a contract is the recent case of *Lombard North Central PLC* v *Butterworth* (1987). This case involved a leasing agreement for a computer, and the contract stated that punctual payment of each quarterly rental was *of the essence* of the contract. The contract then went on to provide that the supplier of the computer would be entitled to re-possess it in the event of failure to make punctual payment, and that in the event of re-possession, all arrears, and future rentals, as well as damages, would be payable by the hirer. When a dispute arose, the hirer denied any intention to repudiate the contract, and argued that the breaches by him of the conditions as to payment were not sufficiently severe to merit the consequences set out in the contract. The Court of Appeal held, however, that the way in which this particular contract had been written, with each time for payment being described as being of the essence, meant that any breach of these particular terms as to payment had to be treated as a serious breach (a breach of condition), and thus the damages would be assessed *as if* there had been a repudiation. It should be noted that this area is fraught with difficulties, not least of which are restrictions upon a seller's or supplier's rights under the Consumer Credit Act 1974, and legal advice on all matters concerning conditions of sale and hire, and payment, is essential.

Damages

A buyer who wrongfully repudiates his obligations under a contract may be liable for damages. In a sale of goods contract this would occur where a buyer attempted to cancel a contract without justification, or where he refused to take delivery of the goods, without good reason. In a building or engineering contract for work and materials, this might occur if an employer were to refuse access to site to the contractor, or to fail in some other important obligation. In a hire contract, as in the case in the preceding paragraph, it would occur if the hirer were to fail to pay hire charges in such a way as to amount to a repudiation. In all these cases the seller or contractor or supplier of hired goods would be entitled to claim such damages as would reflect the loss caused by the breach of contract.

'Break' clauses: no breach of contract is involved

There are certain forms of contract which actually *permit* the employer or buyer to cancel the contract or a part of it. If this form of contract is used, a cancellation which falls within the permissive provisions will not amount to a breach of contract. The contract may, however, contain other related provisions which confer certain financial rights upon the seller or contractor. These rights may fall under definite formulae, so that it is possible to calculate in advance of a cancellation exactly what will be due to the seller, or in some cases, as in many

29

government contracts or defence contracts, there may be provisions which indemnify the seller for unavoidable losses, and provide for fair and reasonable prices for work done during the period mentioned in the notice determining the contract, and provide that claims may be made by the seller for reasonable allowances in cases of hardship. These hardship payments will be largely discretionary, since they will depend upon the buyer being satisfied that hardship exists. Clauses of this kind in government contracts and in defence contracts are often described as 'break' clauses.

If a buyer is in *breach* of contract by cancelling the contract or part of it, the seller will be entitled to claim for **damages**. Damages will depend upon a number of factors, which can only be assessed by looking at the full circumstances of each case. One must, for example, take into account advance or stage payments. One must also take into account the type of goods involved in the contract, and the question of whether or not there is an available market for them if the seller has to re-sell them. Other costs, such as having to store goods, pack and unpack them, modify them, etc, can also be claimed in most circumstances by the seller. Basically the seller is entitled to be placed in the same position, as far as is possible, as he would have been in if the contract had not been broken. No easy rule of thumb can be given because of the number of variables that exist in the many fields of commerce. One thing that should be noted, however, is that under the 'duty to mitigate one's loss', the seller should act reasonably and take reasonable steps to try to reduce his loss.

In a building or construction contract, if a buyer repudiates the contract so that the seller or contractor is unable to complete the work, the seller or contractor may claim damages on the principles mentioned. However, it has been held by the courts that as an alternative to this, the contractor may elect not to claim for damages, but instead to claim for a quantum meruit in respect of the work actually done. If the work done is of considerable value (for example in a case where the contract price is on the low side) the quantum meruit may provide a higher sum for the contractor. However, this depends very much upon the available evidence as to what would be fair and reasonable rates for the work done.

Action for the price

An unpaid seller may bring an action for the price if it is due and not paid, or if, as explained above, the buyer has repudiated his obligations and the seller or contractor elects to claim a quantum meruit, which is a fair and reasonable price for the work done. To claim the price the seller or contractor will have to demonstrate that it is actually *due*. This can often be a question of interpretation of the contract, or more accurately, a question of appraisal of the work or goods to see if they meet the obligations of the contractor. As we saw in *Bolton* v *Mahadeva*, the fact that an installation is in place and commissioned does not necessarily mean that the price is due. Furthermore, in a contract for the *sale of goods*, under the Sale of Goods Act 1979, the seller may bring an action for the price only if the property in the goods has passed to the buyer. This somewhat arcane provision means that in practice, in a contract for the sale of goods, a seller will be able to claim the price where the buyer accepts the goods, and gains title, and then fails to pay. But in those cases where a buyer cancels the order, and is thereby in breach of contract, the seller will not be able to claim the price, but will be confined to a claim for *damages*, because the property will not have passed to the buyer. This rule is of some significance where title to goods is retained by the seller after delivery, since, if the title has not passed to the buyer, the seller presumably would not be able to bring an action to claim the price. It is thought, however, that there may be ways of avoiding this difficulty by specific provisions in the contract, which either make the price payable on a definite date (known as a *day certain*) irrespective of delivery, or else which entitle the seller to maintain an action for the price irrespective of the passing of the property in the goods.

Interest

Sellers sometimes provide in their conditions of contract for interest to be paid on sums that are due and not yet paid. If sellers wish to charge interest in respect of late payment, they must either make provision in the contract, or else be prepared to sue for recovery of the debt, in which case the court is empowered to award interest. Apart from this, there is, as the law stands at present, no right to charge interest in respect of default in payment under a contract of sale. Provisions relating to interest appearing in *invoices* are of no use at all, unless they simply restate what has already been agreed in the *contract*.

Interest may be stated as a figure related to the base rate of a particular bank: for example the base rate of Barclays Bank + 3 or 4%, or it may be stated as a simple percentage, not linked to any other rate. Both methods are in common use in commercial contracts. If the simple percentage is used, it is common to state it as a monthly rate, such as 2%, rather than as an annual rate. However, the main *legal* requirement in formulating one's clause, is clarity and freedom from ambiguity.

Not every seller of goods will include an interest provision in his conditions of contract, and even those sellers who do include such clauses in their contracts will often hesitate to enforce them. This is very much a matter for commercial judgment, as is the selection of an appropriate rate of interest to set down in the contract. There is no point in setting a high rate of interest if one would hesitate to enforce it, when one might have been prepared to enforce a lower rate. On the other hand, too low a rate of interest will give the debtor no incentive to pay promptly. The rule against *penalties* must be kept in mind: for interest to be enforceable, it must not be unreasonable or penal. There are few guidelines on this matter, but obviously commercial norms should be followed. Further notes on the rule against penalties will appear in the next chapter, dealing with delivery.

Termination of the contract on the grounds of delay in payment

To fail to pay when the price (or a part of it) is due is a breach of contract. This, as we have already seen, may give a seller or contractor certain rights, such as the exercise of a lien over the goods. In some cases the seller or contractor may wish to avail himself of one of the most serious remedies, which is the termination of the contract. However, the law has long recognised that in a contract of sale of goods, or in a building or engineering contract, it would have very unfortunate consequences for purchasers if their contracts could be terminated for every failure to pay, no matter how small. The result, as far as contracts of the type with which we are dealing are concerned, is that we can only state whether or not a failure to pay, or a delay in payment justifies a termination of the contract when we know precisely what kind of failure or delay we are talking about, and what the terms of the particular contract are.

If time for payment is *of the essence*, then a failure to pay when the contract provides for payment will be treated strictly, and the seller or contractor will be entitled to treat the contract as being at an end. However, in commercial contracts, time for payment is *not* normally of the essence (although there are exceptions, as where payment is due under a letter of credit against shipping documents). In any contract, it is possible to state expressly, in the conditions of contract, that time for payment shall be of the essence. In the absence of such an express statement, the court *could infer* that time for payment is of the essence, but these are likely to be exceptional cases.

Apart from a statement that time for payment is of the essence, a contract may contain a list of express grounds for termination of the contract (by either party). If the seller or contractor has stated in the contract that failure to pay by a certain date, or after certain notice has been given, entitles him to bring the contract to an end, or to suspend the work, then this will be a ground for suspension or termination. These provisions exist in some standard forms of building contract, and require careful interpretation. If, for example, *a failure to pay an amount certified for payment* by an architect, is an express ground for termination of the contract by the contractor, this will be interpreted strictly to mean a failure to pay *the amount certified*. Thus, the contractor will *not* be entitled to terminate the contract simply because he disagrees with the amount certified, even if there is in fact an error in the certificate. This was the position in *Lubenham Fidelities and Investment Co Ltd* v *South Pembrokeshire District Council* (1986). In this case, interim certificates had been issued, which wrongly showed that liquidated damages had been deducted. The contractor terminated the contracts for alleged breach by the council, and ordered the sub-contractors to cease work. The court held that the contractor had no right to terminate the contract or to suspend the works: where a certificate for payment had been issued, the obligation of the employer was to pay the sums stated. If the contractor believed this amount to have been incorrectly stated, then the proper solution, under this form of contract, was to have the errors remedied by adjustments in subsequent certificates. The employer had not repudiated its obligations here: it was in fact the contractor who had repudiated by indicating an intention not to be bound by the contracts.

Repudiation

A repudiation of a person's obligations under a contract entitles the other person to treat the contract as being at an end. Where the obligation in question is the duty to pay, a repudiation would consist of a person making it clear that he is unable or unwilling to pay, or a person delaying payment to such an extent that it shows an intention not to perform his part of the contract. In the case of a repudiation, it is not necessary for time to be of the essence: the repudiation itself is sufficient to make the breach a serious one, which will permit the other party to end the contract. However, it is necessary in all cases to have sufficient evidence to prove that there has actually been a repudiation. The *Lubenham Fidelities* case already referred to is a clear illustration of this point. Furthermore, in sale of goods contracts, the seller is *not* entitled to treat a mere failure by the buyer to pay as a repudiation (unless time for payment has been made of the essence). This affects the seller's right to sell the goods to another party: the mere exercise of a right of lien does *not* of itself give rise to a right of resale. In fact, the unpaid seller may only resell the goods either if they are perishables, or if the contract sets down a time within which the unpaid seller may resell the goods, or if *notice of intention to resell the goods* has been given to the buyer. This requirement of notice is important because it emphasises the fact that the breach by the buyer must be a serious one in order for the seller to be able to draw the inference that the buyer has repudiated his contract.

3 Delivery and Completion

Commercial contracts may and should contain terms about delivery or completion of work. In the absence of express terms, it may be possible to imply certain terms, but to avoid any doubt it is best for parties to make their intentions clear by express written terms. Such terms could include:

method of delivery
place of delivery
responsibility for loading and unloading
terms about packaging
terms about marking and labelling
times or schedules for delivery
times or programmes for completion of work
buyer's rights in respect of delay
liquidated damages
extension of time

In contracts for the sale of goods, the *Sale of Goods Act 1979* states that it is the duty of the seller to deliver the goods, and of the buyer to accept and pay for them in accordance with the terms of the contract. The Act goes on to *imply* certain terms which will apply unless the parties agree otherwise. These terms include the term that if no time for delivery is fixed, then delivery is to be within a reasonable time. The Act also states that apart from any provisions to the contrary, delivery is to be at the *seller's* place of business. If the contract is not one of sale of goods, but one of work and materials or services, then the *Supply of Goods and Services Act 1982* applies, and provides for certain terms unless the parties make provision to the contrary. For example, if there is no time fixed for the supply of the service, it will be implied that the supplier will carry out the service within a reasonable time. What is a reasonable time is a question of fact, and will depend upon the circumstances of each case, but the point of putting these terms into legislation is to make it clear that the mere fact that times for delivery, or completion of services have not been fixed, does not render a contract unenforceable.

However, if the parties are *negotiating* the terms of the contract, and if it is clear that important matters, such as prices or terms of delivery are a point of *disagreement* in the negotiations, then it will not be possible to imply terms, because to do so would not reflect the legal and commercial realities of the situation. There will not be a contract until the point of disagreement is resolved. This was the position in the case of *British Steel Corporation* v *Cleveland Bridge and Engineering Co Ltd* (1981), where the judge stated that a sub-contract:

'was plainly in a state of negotiation, not least on the issues of price, delivery dates, and the applicable terms and conditions. In these circumstances it is very difficult to see how BSC, by starting work, bound themselves to any contractual performance ... it is impossible to say with any degree of certainty what the material terms of that contract would be.'

METHODS OF DELIVERY

In the modern world, with methods of delivery closely linked to prices, and to methods of payment, and to matters such as risk and insurance, the parties should always make clear their terms about the method and place of delivery of goods. English law recognises the existence of certain terms or expressions which are in common use nationally and internationally, and the interpretation that English law would give to these terms is broadly consistent with their internationally accepted meaning, or the meaning that the International Chamber of Commerce gives to them (INCOTERMS). However, the English courts do *not* treat these meanings as hard and fast rules. English law has long recognised that expressions such as CIF or FOB may be used with a great deal of flexibility, and that behind the expressions there may be many varieties of obligations. Thus the terms described below must always be taken with the *caveat* that the *details* or *context* of a particular contract may make it quite different from other contracts carrying the same description such as CIF or FOB. The list below is not exhaustive.

Ex works   Delivery *ex works* means that the seller has to make the goods available at his works or factory or other premises. It is then up to the buyer to transport the goods. Responsibility for loading the goods onto the vehicle of the buyer is that of the buyer, unless otherwise agreed.

FOR/FOT   These initials mean *Free on Rail* and *Free on Truck* respectively. 'Truck' in this context means a *railway* wagon, so that the expressions should be used only where rail is to be the means of carriage.

FAS   This is *Free Alongside Ship*. Under a contract made on these terms, the seller must place the goods alongside the designated ship, on the quay. At this point, risk, and all further costs involved in export are on the buyer.

FOB   These initials stand for *Free on Board*. The seller's duty is to deliver the goods to a port of shipment named by the buyer, and to have the goods placed on board a ship nominated by the buyer, for the account of the buyer, and to procure a bill of lading in terms usual in the trade. This was described by Mr Justice DEVLIN (as he then was) in *Pyrene Company Ltd* v *Scindia Steam Navigation Company Ltd* (1954) as the 'classic type' of FOB. Mr Justice DEVLIN noted that in modern times the FOB contract has become a 'flexible instrument', and that there are other versions of the FOB. In some cases the seller will make the necessary shipping arrangements, instead of the buyer, and the bill of lading will be in the seller's name, instead of the buyer's, and payment will be against the bill of lading, as in a CIF contract. In other cases the buyer's forwarding agent will book the space on the ship, and the seller will simply place the goods on board and obtain a mate's receipt and hand this to the forwarding agent, so as to enable the forwarding agent to obtain a bill of lading.

Risk in FOB contracts is generally on the buyer when the goods have been lifted over the ship's rail. The seller must give notice to the buyer to enable the buyer to take out any usual insurance of the goods during their sea transit.

FOB airport This is similar to FOB. The seller's duties are fulfilled when he hands the goods to the air carrier at the airport of departure. Risk then passes to the buyer.

CIF These initials mean *Cost, Insurance, Freight.* Under a CIF contract, the seller must make out an invoice of the goods sold; ship goods of the contract description at the port of shipment; procure the contract of carriage by sea, and pay the costs and freight necessary to bring the goods to their port of destination; arrange for insurance upon terms current in the trade, such insurance to be available for the benefit of the buyer; and tender to the buyer the bill of lading, invoice, and insurance policy. The insurance premium will normally be paid by the seller, although there is a form of contract known as C & F (*Cost and Freight*) which is similar to CIF, but under which the buyer will be responsible for the arrangement of the insurance.

Risk in the goods passes on shipment. The property in the goods normally passes when the documents are handed over to the buyer. The bill of lading is a document which is not only evidence of shipment, but which also entitles the buyer, once he is in possession of it, to collect the goods. It will normally be handed over in return for the price on a 'cash against documents' basis. This means that the buyer must pay, or, if letters of credit are used, the correspondent bank must pay, *when the shipping documents are handed over*. Money cannot be withheld until the goods arrive or have been inspected: as long as the documents are in order payment must be made. The 'correspondent bank', in this context, is the bank where the credit is opened in the seller's favour (eg a UK bank, if the seller is in the UK). The 'issuing bank' is the bank instructed by the buyer to open a credit in favour of the seller (eg the buyer's own bank in the buyer's own country). The buyer thus instructs the issuing bank and the issuing bank instructs the correspondent bank. A 'confirmed' credit is one where the *correspondent bank,* as well as the issuing bank, undertakes liability to the seller. Once a letter of credit is confirmed, the bank confirming it must pay the seller against the shipping documents if the documents are in order. The bank is not concerned with any dispute between the buyer and the seller. Thus in *Hamzeh Malas and Sons* v *British Imex Industries Ltd* (1958) the buyer, who alleged that goods shipped were not of the contract quality, was not able to restrain the bank from paying against the documents under a letter of credit. Disputes between the buyer and the seller, in these circumstances, must be dealt with separately.

Ex ship Here the seller must arrange for delivery to the buyer at the port of delivery. The seller therefore has to arrange for carriage by sea and insurance, and pay for these. The risk and property in the goods remain with the seller until the goods are delivered to the buyer. Unlike a CIF contract, payment is not against documents, and the buyer is not bound to pay until he has the goods or the means of obtaining the release of the goods from the ship. Delivery to the buyer is on board the ship, at its destination.

Ex quay   This is similar to ex ship, except that the seller must make the goods available to the buyer on the quay or wharf at the port of destination.

It should always be made clear in the contract which party has the duty to pay duties and clear the goods for import.

As will be seen from the above headings, the type of contract entered into can have an important effect upon the risks, as well as property rights of the parties. And of course it can have an even more sensitive bearing on the question of price. Neither buyer nor seller should enter into contracts of these kinds without having weighed carefully their implications and the duties placed upon the parties, and the effect upon costs, particularly if the unforeseen occurs.

TIME FOR DELIVERY OR COMMENCEMENT OR COMPLETION OF WORK

A good contract is one which has a clear programme. This programme may be of benefit to both parties to the contract, since it need not relate solely to times for delivery, but can relate to the obligations of both parties, such as times for the **approval** of drawings, times for the delivery of **free-issued** goods (ie goods to be supplied by the employer or his agents), time for performance of **tests**, time for **rectification** of defects, time for the giving of **instructions**, etc, and time for making a site or other facility available to the contractor. There is no legal obligation to specify particular times for any of these matters in a contract, but for commercial and practical reasons it is highly desirable that the parties should do so as far as possible. Similarly, when we come to look at the ways in which the law can be used to enforce obligations about time, we should recognise that there is no reason why businesses should necessarily use legal sanctions to obtain goods or services within the time specified: there are bound to be occasions when **commercial** pressures (such as the desire of a seller to obtain a repeat order) are just as effective as the threat of legal action, if not more so. But commercial pressures do not always work, so a good contract should address itself to the legal measures which might have to be taken in the event of a delay which causes loss or expense to either party.

In this chapter we will look at times or programmes of delivery or completion from the point of view of the seller's obligations to the buyer. In a later chapter of this work we will examine in more detail questions of progress, with particular reference to those duties which an employer or buyer may owe to the contractor or seller.

Provisions in a contract relating to time for delivery or for commencement or completion of work do not always appear in the same place in the contract. There may, for example, be a completion date or schedule in one part of the contract, and a clause explaining or qualifying the completion date in another part of the contract, and clauses on liquidated damages and extensions of time in other parts of the same contract. It may therefore be helpful to approach a contract by looking for the following provisions:

PARTICULARS OF THE DELIVERY TERMS
OR OTHER OBLIGATIONS   eg delivery to site, or FOB,etc

TIMES   Whether or not definite dates or schedules are given. Whether or not they are *terms of the contract*. Whether they are qualified or subject to other factors

THE STRENGTH OF THE UNDERTAKINGS   Is time for
AS TO TIME   delivery, etc
                                          'of the essence' ? or not 'of the essence' ?

THE REMEDIES OF THE OTHER PARTY IN
THE EVENT OF DELAY   Rejection of goods,   Damages, and/or
                                          termination of the   any expressly
                                          contract, damages,   specified remedies
                                          and any other expressly
                                          specified remedies

PROVISIONS FOR EXTENSION OF TIME AND/
OR EXCLUSION OF LIABILITY FOR DELAY   Force majeure clauses, or other clauses
                                          dealing with circumstances beyond the
                                          parties' control. Clauses excluding lia-
                                          bility for delay or consequential loss
                                          caused by delay

These headings may now be explained. The **particulars of the delivery terms and other obligations** are important, because if times are to be given, we need to be accurate about what it is that the seller or contractor is required to achieve within the given time. It is no use a seller having goods merely loaded onto a ship within a given time, if the contract is for delivery *ex ship* within that time; nor is it any use achieving delivery to a site within a given time, if the contract is for commissioning and passing of tests after delivery to site within that same period of time. In the case of a contract to ship goods, a seller may find that there are certain areas to which it is not advisable to promise to ship goods and deliver ex ship by a given date, because of factors which make the timing too unpredictable. The seller may therefore decide that if time is to be made an important term of the contract, he will offer FOB terms but not ex ship.

The **times** discussed by a buyer and seller, or employer and contractor, during the negotiations leading up to a contract, may or may not end up as part of the contract. This depends upon what is agreed upon by the parties. It is possible that they may agree that times are subject to so many variable factors that they are no more than estimates. Sellers who draft their own conditions of sale sometimes make it clear in those conditions that times stated are approximate only, *and not terms of the contract at all*. If this is agreed, then there will be no delivery date or programme, because there is no such term of the contract. However, there will still be the *implied* term that delivery or the carrying out of the service will be within a reasonable time. The approximate date or time will then be a *guideline* as to what is a reasonable time, but not strictly binding between the parties.

It is more common for the parties to contract on the basis that the times stated for delivery, etc, are *terms of the contract*. If this is so, then it is a binding obligation to do what was promised on or within the time stated. A failure to do so is a *breach of contract*. However, two points must be made about this. One is the important point that not all breaches of contract have the same consequences, because much will depend upon the strength of the term and the gravity of the breach. This point will be dealt with in detail in the paragraph which follows. The second point is that *some* (but not all) contracts make it clear that there may be reasons for the delay, and that if any of the stated reasons holds good, such as a failure by the employer to give certain instructions or approvals or details which are required under the contract, then the delay will not involve a breach of contract by the seller or contractor, and he will be entitled to extend the delivery date to take account of these factors.

Undertakings as to time: is time for delivery or completion 'of the essence' or 'not of the essence'?

Undertakings as to time in a contract must be performed, regardless of the strength of the undertaking in question. However, the nature or strength of the undertaking is highly relevant in deciding what **remedy** is available in the event of a failure to perform on time or according to programme. The distinction between those times that are of the essence and those that are not of the essence was made in the chapter on payment, and a few paragraphs earlier in this chapter. If a time is described in a contract as being of the essence, *or* if it can be *inferred* as being of the essence from the *context* of the contract, then it is an *important term* (called by lawyers *a condition*) of the contract, v...ereas if it is not of the essence, then it is a term of the contract, but it is not important enough for every breach of it to be described as a breach of condition. The result of this distinction is that *every* breach of a time which is of the essence is serious enough to warrant not only a claim for damages by the other party, but also a claim to treat the contract as being at an end. Whereas, if a term about time is not of the essence, a breach of it will give rise to a claim for damages, but *not* to a right to treat the contract as being at an end, *unless* the contract specifically provides for such a remedy, or *unless* the breach is so great as to amount to a repudiation by the seller.

How does time become 'of the essence'?

This can occur in several ways. Firstly, it can be expressly stated in the contract. Secondly, it can be inferred from the words used by the parties and the circumstances of the contract. Thirdly, even where a time *did not start* as being of the essence, it is possible, after a breach by the seller of the original time, that the buyer can *make time of the essence*, by giving reasonable notice to the seller as soon as the default has occurred. This last point is by no means free from doubt, but it is supported by eminent writers and by authority of some courts, on the basis that once a party is already in default, there is no reason why he should not be given notice to perform within a reasonable time or risk having the contract terminated.

Examples of times that were of the essence

Kolfer Plant Hire Ltd v Tilbury Plant Ltd (1977)

In this case, the seller agreed, in an oral contract made on 5 February 1974, to sell to the buyer a diesel generator, which was to be delivered to the premises of a third party by 6 February 1974. The order stated that it was required *at the latest* on 7 February 1974. It was not in fact delivered until 8 February 1974, by which time it was no longer needed. The customer refused to pay the price, and rejected the machine, which, in the meantime, had to be stored. The customer also claimed damages for the cost of removing and storing the machine. The court dismissed the action for the price, and upheld the counterclaim for damages. The customer had been entitled to reject the goods in this case, because it could be inferred from the nature and circumstances of this contract, and the words used by the parties, that *time for delivery was of the essence*.

McDougall v Aeromarine of Emsworth Ltd (1958)

In this case the contract was for the manufacture and sale of a boat. A clause in the written contract stated that the builders would use their best endeavours to complete by 1 May 1957, but it also stated that the delivery date could not be guaranteed. The buyer paid by instalments during the period of construction. After a trial run, the buyer refused to take delivery due to the unfitness of the boat. This was in accordance with the contract terms which provided that the buyer could withhold approval on certain grounds, and refuse to take delivery. By September 1957, the boat was still not ready. The buyer now rejected it, on the grounds of delay, and claimed the return to him of the payments made. The court held that the buyer was entitled to do this. The date of 1 May 1957 was not strictly binding, since the contract stated that it was not guaranteed, but on a proper interpretation of the contract, delivery *was due within a reasonable time of 1 May 1957, and this time was of the essence*.

From these two cases, it will be understood that not a great deal is required in a contract of sale of goods to give rise to the inference that *time for delivery* is of the essence. It is a matter of evidence as to the intentions or the parties: as the Sale of Goods Act 1979 states, it 'depends on the terms of the contract'.

On the other hand, in a building or construction contract, time will probably *not* be interpreted as being of the essence unless the contract contains express provisions on this point. This, again, is a matter of interpretation of the particular contract, but without clear provisions making time of the essence, it would in most cases be unreasonable to imagine that the parties intended an employer to be entitled to cancel the contract on the grounds of *any* delay, no matter how small. The consequences would be severe for the contractor, who would run the risk of being dismissed on the grounds of delay, and who might not be able to recover any payment. Thus in most cases a building contract will be interpreted as one where time is not of the essence, and the effect will be that the employer will normally have to accept work which is completed after the date scheduled for completion, and claim for, or deduct, *damages* for the delay. This is of course consistent with the fact that many building and engineering contracts contain *liquidated damages* clauses, which envisage that the employer will be prepared to accept work that is completed after the scheduled completion date, but will deduct or recover damages on an agreed scale in respect of the delay. It is possible *to make time of the essence* in any kind of contract, including building and engineering contracts, by express words in the contract. But this does not always serve the desired purpose, since the way in which a time which is of the essence works is as follows: the employer will have to wait *until the date scheduled for completion has been passed*; he will then be entitled to terminate the contract on account of failure by the contractor to complete on time. By this time, in practice, it would in many cases do little good to the employer to terminate the contract, since it would not necessarily follow that he would be able to find any other person who would be able to complete the work more quickly. What the employer really needs is the right to terminate a contract, and to replace a contractor who is unwilling or unable to complete the work on time, *well before the scheduled completion date*. This will not be achieved by a clause making time of the essence, but it can be achieved by means of a clear programme of work, and express **provisions** which entitle the employer to terminate the contract in the event of failure by the contractor to make due and diligent progress with the work. These provisions sometimes appear in building and engineering contracts under the heading of 'determination by the employer', or other similar headings. Such clauses should always be scrutinised carefully, since they tend to differ on matters of detail, such as the precise grounds for determination, and the procedures to be followed, such as the giving of notice by the employer to the contractor. Express provisions requiring the giving of notice must be followed, and it is a matter of construction whether notice should be given before an employer is entitled to determine the contract.

In *Wickman Tools* v *Schuler AG* (1974) the contract in question provided that either of the parties could determine the contract if the other party had committed a material breach of its obligations, and had failed to remedy the same within 60 days of being required in writing to do so. A different clause in the same contract placed firm obligations upon the contractor, and these obligations were described as 'conditions', that is, important terms of the contract. There were breaches of the obligations described as 'conditions', and the question was whether or not the employer was entitled to determine the contract without notice and without giving the contractor the opportunity to put matters right. The House of Lords held that it was proper and reasonable to construe both clauses of the contract together, so that notice had to be given, in the event of a material breach of the contract, including a breach of the obligations described as 'conditions', and the contract could only be terminated if the breaches were not remedied within the period of notice.

LIQUIDATED DAMAGES

It is fairly common for contracts to provide that certain sums of money shall be paid or deducted from the price in the event of a delay in delivering goods or in completing work to be done under the contract. These sums are known as 'liquidated' damages because they are damages that are agreed and estimated when the contract is made. There is no compulsion to have a liquidated damages clause in a contract, but in building and engineering contracts they are often found, because the parties may have agreed that there should be such provisions in the contract. Either party may have an interest in seeing to it that the contract contains a liquidated damages clause. The employer may want the benefit of such a clause, in so far as it gives specific powers to deduct specific sums from the price, or to recover specific sums. This not only facilitates financial remedies for the employer, but also gives a disincentive as regards delay by the contractor. From the employer's point of view, perhaps the most valuable point about liquidated damages is that proof of the extent of the damage or loss suffered due to the delay is not needed, because the clause has already *agreed upon the* measure of damages.

From the contractor's point of view, liquidated damages may present a serious problem, since the contractor runs the risk that he may fall into delay and suffer deductions from the price, or even an action for recovery over and above the price. This risk exists in cases where the contractor accepts liquidated damages provisions in the contract without any limit on liability, and without sufficient protection against circumstances which are beyond his control. In practice, not many contractors are willing to accept such risks, and if they accept liquidated damages provisions in the contract they will aim to limit their liability to an acceptable amount, such as 5%, or 10% of the contract price. They will also aim to protect themselves against circumstances beyond their control, by means of provisions which will entitle them to apply for an extension of time in certain circumstances, and to reduce or eliminate the period of delay.

Thus the negotiation of provisions about liquidated damages is, like the negotiation of other matters in the contract, a matter of the parties being able to reach an agreed position. Once the provisions, and the contract, have been agreed, they are binding on both parties. Buyers and employers are bound by the scales or sums agreed upon as liquidated damages, even if it turns out that they have underestimated their losses. This was decided by the House of Lords in the case of *Widnes Foundry Ltd* v *Cellulose Acetate Silk Co Ltd* (1931), which concerned the delivery and construction of an acetone recovery plant. The contract provided for £20 as liquidated damages for each week of delay. The delay was 30 weeks. The purchasers claimed £5,850 as damages for the delay, but the House of Lords held that the figure of £600 was the proper sum, since this was what had been agreed in the liquidated damages clause. There could perhaps be exceptional cases where the employer might be able to recover a larger sum than the liquidated damages, if that was provided for by the contract, but this was not one of those cases.

For a liquidated damages provision to be effective, the following things are required. Firstly, there must be a clause in a contract stating the matter for which liquidated damages are to be paid or deducted. This will normally be for delay in delivery or delay in completion of work by the contractor, but liquidated damages could be stated to be payable on account of other matters, such as deficiencies in the *performance* of plant or machinery. Secondly, the contract must refer to a definite completion or delivery date or period. If it is a period rather than a date, then it must be clear from when the period is to run. Thirdly, the contract must refer to a definite sum or scale of damages to be paid or deducted in the event of delay. This may be done by means of a fixed sum to be payable or deductible in respect of stated periods of delay, such as £1,000 per week of delay. Or, alternatively, the contract may refer to a percentage of the contract price or value, which is to be paid or deducted in respect of stated periods of delay, such as 0.5% of the contract price for each week of delay.

The rule against penalties

Apart from the above requirements for liquidated damages to be effectively provided for, there is one further requirement, and that is that the liquidated damages provisions must not offend against the rule against penalties. This rule does not exist in every legal system, but it is a most important principle of English law, so much so that although those in business or engineering or building may speak informally of 'penalties', they would *not* be advised to use this word in a contract if what was really meant was 'liquidated damages'. Lord DIPLOCK stated the modern law on this subject in the case of *Photo Production Ltd* v *Securicor Ltd* (1980):

> 'Parties are free to agree to whatever exclusion or modification of all types of obligations as they please within the limits that the agreement must retain the legal characteristics of a contract and must not offend against the equitable rule against penalties; that is to say, it must not impose upon the breaker of a primary obligation a general secondary obligation to pay to the other party a sum of money which is manifestly intended to be in excess of the amount which would fully compensate the other party for the loss sustained by him in consequence of the breach of the primary obligation.'

Thus liquidated damages must not be expressed in such a way that they could work in an arbitrary, or harsh, or oppressive manner. The rule against penalties does not mean that complete accuracy of foresight is needed on the part of the parties when they decide upon the sums or scale of damages that are to be payable. But it does mean that the sums, or scale, as the case may be, must be *genuine pre-estimates* of the likely loss to the buyer in the event of a breach by the seller. If the courts interpret a provision in a contract as a penalty, the offending provision will be void, although the rest of the contract may be unaffected. This will then mean that the employer will be unable to rely upon liquidated damages as a remedy, but he will retain his common law right to sue *for such damages as he can prove to have been caused by the delay*. This will then present the employer with a burden of proof, and if his damage is in fact less than the amount provided for in the liquidated damages clause, he will be unable to claim as much as he would have been able to claim had the clause not been construed as a penalty.

The concept of penalties applies to most kinds of contract, including contracts of sale, hire, hire-purchase, loans, building contracts, engineering contracts, contracts of employment, etc. Thus sellers and contractors should be aware that any sanctions which they might seek to apply against their customers, for example in the event of non-payment, would be subject to the same principles: they must not be such as would seek to extract from the other party greater compensation than the amount that is needed to make good the loss caused by the breach of contract.

Bramall and Ogden Ltd v *Sheffield City Council* (1983)
The parties had entered into a building contract in the JCT 1963 form, with 1973 revision, for the construction of 123 houses. The contract provided for liquidated damages at the rate of £20 per week for each uncompleted dwelling. The employer claimed to deduct liquidated damages. The court held that liquidated damages could not be deducted here, since the clause in question operated as a penalty. The reason for this was that because of the way in which the contract was written, the employer would be entitled to deduct liquidated damages in respect of *all* the dwellings, at the rate provided, regardless of the fact that the employer had in fact taken possession of some of the houses earlier then others.

It may be that a sum stated to be liquidated damages is larger than the loss that follows from a particular delay on a particular occasion. This happens frequently in building and engineering contracts, when goods or materials are delivered late, but the circumstances of the particular delay are such that it does not in fact disrupt a project seriously, or cause any serious loss. The fact that no great loss is suffered does not of itself make the liquidated damages into a penalty. The test is whether or not the sum stipulated is excessive in relation to the *greatest loss that could have followed from the breach*.

Liquidated damages cannot be enforced unless there is an agreed time or date for delivery or completion, and it may be that for some reason, in a particular contract, the date for delivery or completion becomes inapplicable and ceases to be enforceable. Examples of this would be where the employer interferes with the performance of the contract, or fails in his own obligations under the contract and thereby causes delay. Clearly the seller or contractor cannot be blamed for the delay caused by these circumstances, and so he will not be liable to liquidated damages on this account. However, the question which then arises is whether or not the employer will be able to adjust the completion date or period, to take account of the disruption, and thereby be able to 're-set' the date from which liquidated damages may run. If the employer were not able to do this, his position would be seriously weakened after any default on his own part, or even after the ordering of extras, since he would no longer have the protection of a liquidated damages clause. The way in which employers cope with this is by specific extension of time clauses.

Liquidated damages cannot be enforced against the seller or contractor if any matters specified in an extension of time clause, or 'force majeure' clause, are the cause of the delay. Thus, if strikes are specified or included within such a clause, and if a strike causes a delay of, for example, 60 days, then a time extension of 60 days will be due to the contractor, and he will not be liable for liquidated damages for this period. It follows that the wording of extension of time clauses, or 'force majeure' clauses, requires considerable attention by both parties. If the circumstances in which an extension of time is to be granted are too widely defined, the contractor will have wide scope for escaping liability for delay (a point which applies even if there is no liquidated damages clause, since the contractor will then seek to escape from other forms of liability for delay). If the circumstances are insufficiently defined, the employer could find his own position prejudiced, since there have been cases where employers have wanted to grant extensions of time so as to re-set the completion date and preserve their right to liquidated damages, and have found that the contract did not permit them to do so. These points will be dealt with in chapter 9.

4 Title to Goods

In this chapter we examine the significance for commercial and building and engineering contracts of terms governing the passing of property in goods.

Commercial contracts for the sale of goods, as well as building and engineering contracts, usually contain provisions concerning ownership or property in goods or materials. If the contracts contain no such express provisions, then general principles of common law or statutory law will determine who is the owner of goods or materials at any particular time. Ownership or title is one of the fundamentals of commercial law: approximately one fifth of the Sale of Goods Act 1979, for example, is devoted to this issue. In these pages we will set out to examine and clarify the following matters:

1 Why ownership matters, and the legal consequences of ownership or non-ownership of goods or materials.
2 The ways in which terms relating to the passing of property may be expressly formulated.
3 The principles of law which will apply in the absence of any express provisions in the contract.
4 The issue of Retention of Title, and the purposes that clauses retaining title are intended to serve, and the legal and practical problems which may arise in attempting to retain or to enforce the retention of title to goods.

THE LEGAL CONSEQUENCES OF OWNERSHIP

The expressions 'ownership' and 'property' in goods may, for the purposes of this work, be treated as similar in meaning, although in other areas of law there may be subtle differences. In the case of *Clough Mill Ltd* v *Martin* (1984), the Court of Appeal accepted that the expression 'ownership', which appeared in a condition of a contract, stating that 'ownership of the material shall remain with the seller . . .' meant quite simply the property in the goods. Furthermore, unless the contract provides otherwise, 'property' is defined as the general property in goods, not merely a special property.

One of the objects of a contract of sale of goods, or of a building or engineering contract, is to pass the property in goods or materials at some stage from the seller or contractor to the buyer. There are of course commercial contracts with different objectives, such as contracts of *hire*, or *bailment*, under which an owner of goods passes *possession*, but not ownership, to his customer. The essence of hire or bailment is that the hirer or bailee is under a duty to return the goods to the owner. Furthermore, the owner has a title to the goods which can be defended not only against the hirer, but also against third parties.

These concepts have been put to practical use in commercial contracts by those who wish to sell goods but at the same time to have the security of ownership of the goods until payment has been made. A simple example of this is a contract of hire-purchase, which is a contract of hire, with an option to purchase which arises and is exercisable at a particular date or on a particular event occurring.

Until the option to purchase is exercised, the supplier of the goods remains the owner of the goods. Hire-purchase developed many decades ago and has been found to be a particularly suitable vehicle for transactions with consumers and with small businesses. A more sophisticated vehicle for achieving similar ends, particularly in business contracts, has been retention of title. If a seller of goods wishes to contract to sell goods to his customer, but at the same time remain the owner of the goods until he has been paid, it is possible to do this by a suitably worded clause governing the passing of the property in the goods. In essence, the seller states in the contract that while the purchaser is to hold the goods, after delivery, in the capacity of *bailee*, or in some similar capacity, the *ownership* of the goods is to remain with the seller until payment has been made in full. This form of contract has for the purchaser the advantages of being a contract of sale, but it also attempts to give to the seller the security of ownership of the goods. The security is not always perfect, and has sometimes proved to be ineffective for practical purposes, but legally it is an acceptable device, as Lord Justice GOFF stated in *Clough Mill* v *Martin* (1984):

> 'I for my part can see nothing objectionable in an agreement between parties under which A, the owner of goods, gives possession of those goods to B, at the same time conferring on B a power of sale and a power to consume the goods in manufacture, though A will remain the owner of the goods until they are either sold or consumed. I do not see why the relationship between A and B, pending sale or consumption, should not be the relationship of bailor and bailee.'

Having stated that ownership of property is important, we must now take note that it does not always give absolute rights to goods or materials, and there are cases when the owner of goods may find that he is unable to gain possession of them, and even cases when his title may be defeated by the claims of a third party. There are numerous examples, and a few of particular commercial importance will suffice.

The Factors Acts, and the 'Buyer in Possession' rule

A person may have possession of goods without being their owner. Normally he cannot confer any title upon third parties by disposing of those goods. But the law has long recognised exceptions to this rule, and these exceptions exist to protect third parties, and can be justified because the professor of goods often *appears*, in the eyes of the third party, to be the owner. The Factors Acts were enacted in the last century, and they enabled an apparent owner of goods to dispose of the goods as if he were the true owner, provided that certain

47

conditions were satisfied. The apparent owner had to have legitimate possession of the goods with the consent of the true owner, and had to dispose of the goods as a mercantile agent to a person taking them in good faith. The Sale of Goods Act 1979, section 25, applies similar principles where a buyer has acquired *possession*, but *not ownership*, of goods, and disposes of them to a third party. Provided that the necessary conditions are fulfilled, the third party will acquire title, and this will defeat the title of the original owner.

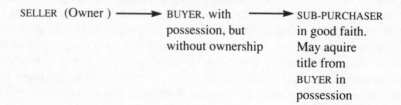

This rule may defeat a retention of title clause which purports to keep ownership in the seller, since it was decided in the case of *Four Point Garage Ltd v Carter* (1984) that when a seller retains title to goods he does not necessarily preclude the right of his purchaser to sell the goods to a third party in the ordinary course of business. The above case concerned a seller which had retained title to a new car which it had contracted to sell, and a purchaser which had disposed of the car to a third party, and had then gone into liquidation. The High Court held that the third party satisfied the necessary conditions imposed by section 25 of the Sale of Goods Act, and had therefore acquired title.

The above case demonstrates an important limit upon the extent to which parties may expressly regulate questions of title by use of conditions of contract. The rights of third parties acting in good faith may intervene and defeat the objectives of the original seller of the goods. One must recognise that this is an almost inevitable fact of commercial law, and take steps accordingly.

Sellers' and contractors' liens

The old saying that possession is nine tenths of the law is, of course, strictly inaccurate, since ownership is rather more valuable than mere possession. Nevertheless there are instances when possession of goods is capable of giving powerful rights even against the owner of the goods. One such instance is when a possessor of goods has a *lien* against those goods. A lien is the right to retain possession of the goods until certain claims or debts have been satisfied. If a seller of goods so agrees, it may be that his buyer becomes owner of the goods prior to delivery. The seller will, however, have a *lien* on those goods, and can, for example, hold them back if the buyer fails to make payment on the due date.

Lien may arise by contract or it may arise by operation of law. Commercial contracts often contain express provisions either creating or preserving a lien on goods, or excluding the lien of another party. Express contractual provisions may also state whether the lien is to be a *general lien* (ie relating to goods generally) or a *particular lien* (ie relating only to the subject matter of the unpaid debt or unsatisfied claim). In the case of *George Barker (Transport) Ltd* v *Eynon* (1974), the Court of Appeal had the opportunity to give an analysis of the concept of lien in a modern commercial context. In this case, a transport contractor accepted orders on the Conditions of Carriage of the Road Haulage Association, which stated that:

> 'The Carrier shall have a general lien against the owner of any goods for any moneys whatsoever due from such owner to the Carrier ...'

The transport contractor was owed money by its customer, and had still to carry out a contract of carriage for that customer. After it had collected the relevant goods, the transport contractor learnt that its customer had had a receiver of its business appointed a few days earlier. The question was whether or not the transport contractor's lien took precedence over the rights of the receiver. The chronology was important in this case, and the court held that since this was a lien created by *contract*, the contractual rights of the transport contractor existed prior to the appointment of the receiver. The contractor may have acquired possession after the appointment of the receiver, but the rights of the receiver, and of those whom he represented, were subject to the pre-existing contractual rights of the contractor, who was therefore entitled to claim the goods to the value of the outstanding debts.

The 'Seller in Possession'

A lien alone does not give to a seller of goods the right to sell to another party goods which have been sold to, and are owned by, his customer. Once again, however, the law has recognised that there must be exceptions made to this rule, so as to protect third parties who rely upon the seller's appearance of being the true owner. This is known as the *Seller in Possession* rule, and appears in the Sale of Goods Act 1979. It operates as follows:

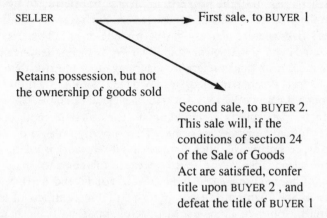

SELLER ⟶ First sale, to BUYER 1

Retains possession, but not
the ownership of goods sold

Second sale, to BUYER 2.
This sale will, if the
conditions of section 24
of the Sale of Goods
Act are satisfied, confer
title upon BUYER 2 , and
defeat the title of BUYER 1

The conditions in section 24 of the Sale of Goods Act 1979 which must be satisfied are that the original seller must have retained *possession* of the goods in question, and must have delivered them or the documents of title to a person acting in good faith without notice of the previous sale.

Furthermore, a seller who has exercised his right of lien (for example because of the failure of the buyer to pay), will have the *right* to resell the goods if he has reserved that right in the contract, or if the goods are perishables, or if he gives to the buyer notice of his intention to resell, and the buyer does not pay within a reasonable time.

Having noted these instances where a mere possessor of goods will have power to withhold them, provided that the necessary conditions exist, or to dispose of them in such a way as to affect the rights of the true owner, we must now return to the basic concept of ownership. In the majority of commercial cases, it is highly desirable that parties should be able to tell who has the ownership of goods and materials. To give some examples:

(a) A *buyer who has paid in advance* for any goods or materials may wish to know whether or not he has title to those goods, even though they have not yet been delivered. If the buyer can establish ownership, this will be one form of security for his advance payment. If the buyer cannot establish ownership, he may wish to look to other forms of security, such as performance bonds.

(b) A *seller* who is prepared to deliver goods to his buyer, and to give *credit facilities* to that buyer, may wish to know what title to the goods he has after delivery to the buyer. The answer to this question leads us into the complexities of retention of title. At this stage it will suffice to say that without specific provisions establishing that the seller is the owner of the goods, he will, in the case of an ordinary sale of goods, lose title upon delivery. He will then be unable to recover the goods in the event of his buyer's insolvency or failure to pay. His claim will be for a *debt*, but not for the goods.

(c) Either party to a contract involving goods may wish to know where the *risk in those goods* lies at any given moment. Section 20 of the Sale of Goods Act 1979 provides that *unless otherwise agreed*, the goods remain at the seller's risk until the property in them is transferred to the buyer but when the property in them is transferred to the buyer the goods are at the buyer's risk whether delivery has been made or not. Thus risk normally goes hand in hand with ownership. By 'risk' we mean that one party or the other must bear (and preferably insure against) the risk that the goods may be lost, stolen, damaged, or may perish, without fault on either side. Although the Sale of Goods Act states a general principle, it is common in contracts, particularly in building or construction contracts, for the parties to make *express provisions*. This is partly because of the need to place express responsibilities upon parties where work is taking place on a specific site or installation, partly because the contracts may be longer term and more complicated than sales of goods, and partly because the contracts are often not sales of goods at all, but contracts of labour and materials. Contracts involving carriage of goods, particularly carriage of goods by sea, may also contain express or implied conditions which alter the basic rule of section 20 of the Sale of Goods Act. In a CIF contract, for example, it is generally accepted that by common law, the risk in the goods passes to the buyer when the goods are lifted over the ship's rail. However, the *property in the goods* does not necessarily pass to the buyer at this time, for a number of reasons which will be analysed in due course. Thus the general rule that risk passes with property is displaced.

EXPRESS PROVISIONS IN CONTRACTS REGARDING THE PASSING OF PROPERTY

In general the law does not contain any restriction upon the right of parties to a commercial contract to state when the property in goods is to pass. Property may be made to pass on payment, or upon delivery, or upon shipment, or upon the happening of some other specified event. It is for the parties, if they wish, to agree upon a clear provision to which effect can be given. If they do not do so, then the law will have to decide, by inference, or by general principles of law, when the property is to pass. In the next few pages we will examine some of the ways in which the parties may draft or otherwise agree provisions concerning the passing of property, and risk, in goods.

1 Ownership to pass on delivery

This is a standard, and generally acceptable provision. The interests of buyers and sellers (and of employers, main contractors and sub-contractors) are not by any means identical, but on the other hand it does not follow that a fair and reasonable provision governing the ownership of goods cannot be agreed upon. In a standard sale where payment is to be on or soon after delivery, there is often no reason why ownership should not be stated as passing upon delivery. This in fact coincides with the most common of the principles of the law of sale of goods governing this matter. It assumes that in general a buyer will have no great interest in acquiring title to the goods prior to delivery, and the seller will not wish to retain title after delivery, since he will either have given no credit at all, or else will have given credit only to those customers who are creditworthy. These assumptions do not always hold good, however, and where the basic assumptions change, either the seller or the buyer (or main contractor or sub-contractor) may have to consider different ways of arranging for the passing of property.

2 Ownership to pass before delivery

It is possible to draft a contract which states, among other things, that the ownership of goods or materials will pass to the buyer either upon the making of payment, or upon the making of a stage payment, or upon the appropriation of the goods to the contract, or upon the construction of the goods or the allocation or acquisition of materials for construction of the goods. Buyers may wish to formulate and to include provisions of this kind in the contract for financial reasons. Or, particularly in government contracts such as defence contracts, there may well be practical reasons and reasons of policy.

It is important to note that such provisions may be (and are, in Ministry of

Defence contracts) passed on from one contractor to another. This is done by 'back-to-back' contractual clauses under which a main contractor will make an agreement concerning the passing or vesting of property with his customer, and will include in his contract with his sub-contractor a clause which will be formulated so as to ensure that the desired overall result is achieved. This does *not* happen automatically: it is only achievable if the contracts are carefully drafted and formed.

Apart from Ministry contracts, there will be other ordinary commercial situations where a buyer will require conditions of contract which will vest title to goods or materials in him prior to delivery. A buyer may have made advance or stage payments. These can, if necessary, be protected by 'advance payment bonds' or performance bonds. However, where there are no bonds or financial guarantees, a buyer may wish to protect himself by providing for vesting of the property in him on the making of payment or a stage payment. Many buyers are not content merely to state this in the contract, and in addition they will take practical steps, such as securing that the goods are marked or labelled as their property, prior to delivery.

3 Ownership not to pass until the buyer has made payment

This is known generally as *retention of title*. It has always been a possibility, in principle, under the Sale of Goods Act, firstly in its 1893 version, and subsequently the 1979 version. It was in the nineteen seventies and eighties, however, that retention of title became a serious and much contested legal issue. This fact may be ascribed to the sellers' desires to protect themselves from the insolvency of their buyers, and the increasing awareness of sellers and their lawyers that, so long as credit is given, this cannot easily be achieved without reliance upon certain highly specialised conditions of contract. One must emphasise that retention of title clauses in contracts are of a specialised nature, and must be expressly drafted or incorporated into contracts: there is very little chance that the common law will imply a term that a seller is to keep the ownership in the goods after delivery and before payment. The Sale of Goods Act permits the parties to express such a term, but it is then up to the parties to do this in *clear and unmistakable language*. In the case of *Bond Worth* (1979), the seller, Monsanto Ltd attempted to rely upon a retention of title clause in its standard terms of sale. The court held, however, that although the seller had contracted on its standard terms of sale, the clause in question did not mean what the seller had intended it to mean, and since the clause was ineffective, the court then applied principles from the Sale of Goods Act to hold that the property had in fact passed to the buyer. The lesson of *Bond Worth* is that one must always use clear and effective language in one's contracts. Retention of title can be created simply by providing in the contract that the property in the goods shall not pass to the buyer until the goods have been paid for in full. However, behind this simple concept there are a number of significant legal and practical difficulties. These difficulties involve draftsmanship, administration, and the interaction of contract law with the laws of insolvency and Company law. Retention of title has been aptly stated to have become a legal minefield.

There is also the purely commercial question of whether or not a seller will wish to negotiate contracts on this basis, and whether or not the buyer will allow the seller to do so. All these points will be explored at a later stage.

WHEN DOES THE PROPERTY PASS? THE GENERAL PRINCIPLES OF LAW

Meanwhile, we must look at those principles which will apply if the parties do not make express provisions of their own, or if, as in the *Bond Worth* case, the court decides that the attempt to provide for the vesting of title or retention of title is ineffective. The general principles of law are drawn from the Sale of Goods Act 1979, in a contract of sale of goods, and from the common law in other cases. These principles of law are by no means simple: they depend upon the kind of contract and the kind of goods involved, and in the case of contracts of carriage of goods, upon the kind of contract of carriage.

At this stage we may sketch out some of the possible key events in a contract involving the supply of goods or materials.

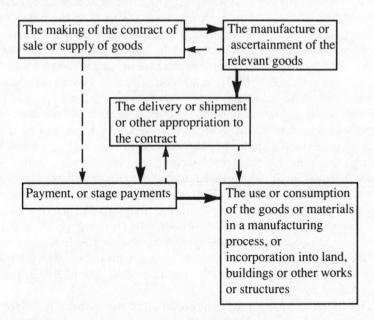

An example of the possible sequence of events is given by the unbroken arrows. A different example is given by the broken arrows. It will at once become apparent that there are numerous possible permutations of the events which may occur, depending upon the commercial arrangements made between the parties. Furthermore, the goods may be simply sold on to other parties. We are asking at all times the simple question: who is the owner of the goods? We may now give some guidance as to how to answer this question, but the point of the diagram is that *all the facts of the particular case must be considered.*

53

The rules are as follows:

(a) The property in goods passes when the parties intend it to pass.

(b) No property in the goods can pass unless the goods are *specific* or until they are *ascertained*. This in effect means that the goods the subject of the contract must exist, and, where goods are held or stored or shipped in bulk, it must be clear which goods are for which buyer. This rule is in the Sale of Goods Act, and was explained in the case of *Karlshamns Oljefabriker* v *Eastport Navigation Corp* (1982), where the judge of the Commercial Court stated 'What is needed for ascertainment is that the buyer should be able to say "Those are my goods".

(c) Payment does not normally pass the property in goods unless this is made a condition of the contract. Thus a buyer who makes advance payments or stage payments does not thereby acquire the property in the goods unless he has so provided in the contract.

(d) It is possible for the ownership of a *specific* item to pass at once, on the making of the contract, irrespective of payment or delivery. This is quite likely to occur in the case of auctions or sales of specific works of art, but it is unlikely to occur often in ordinary commercial sales.

(e) In contracts for the sale of commercial goods, the most common inference to be drawn is that the property in goods will pass to the buyer upon delivery or other appropriation to the contract (see diagram). This rule appears in the Sale of Goods Act itself, but is worded in a somewhat obscure manner, and is explained in the case of *Carlos Federspiel and Co SA* v *Twigg and Co Ltd* (1957). In this case, goods had been manufactured to the order of the buyer and were ready for export. The buyer had paid for the goods in advance. At this point, a receiver of the seller was appointed on behalf of the debenture holders. The buyer was of course entitled to claim as a creditor of the seller. However, the buyer knew well enough that the position of an unsecured creditor was not a particularly advantageous one in which to be, under the circumstances, and consequently the buyer claimed to be the owner of the goods. However, the commercial court held that the property in the goods had not yet passed to the buyer. The court held that although the relevant goods could be identified, they had not yet been *appropriated to the contract*. This was an FOB contract, and the assumption in such a contract was that the goods had not been appropriated to the contract until they had been put on board the ship.

This leaves us asking how, 'appropriation to the contract' is defined. In fact there is no firm legal definition of this concept, and this is one good reason why express terms about the passing of property are highly desirable. Delivery, or shipment in FOB contracts, will normally constitute appropriation. So will a setting aside of the goods together with the giving by the seller to the buyer or his agent of documents of title or documents sufficient to enable the buyer to collect the goods. Anything short of this is liable to be construed as not being an appropriation.

(f) A distinction must now be made between contracts for the *sale of goods*, and those contracts, including building and engineering contracts, which are not strictly sales of goods, but contracts for *work and materials*. If a builder's merchant delivers goods to site under a 'supply only' contract, that is a contract of sale of goods. If a contractor takes goods to site to use in a building or engineering project, the contract will probably be one for work and materials. In the latter instance, the Sale of Goods Act does not apply, because it is not a sale of goods. Instead, the general principles of law regarding contracts for work and materials will apply. Under these principles, we must first of all look at the express provisions of the contract, so as to ascertain the intentions of the parties. If no intention is expressed, the contractor will be presumed to have retained the title in the goods and materials which he has brought onto site for use on the project. The property in those goods will thus remain with the contractor until they are fixed. This was demonstrated in the case of *Dawber Williamson Roofing Ltd* v *Humberside County Council* (1979). In this case Dawber Williamson Roofing Ltd entered into a sub-contract to supply and fix roofing slates. The main contractor had entered into a contract with the local authority. The architect had issued certificates to the main contractor, and the main contractor had received a stage payment in respect of the slates. The main contractor then went into receivership. The contracts terminated. The slates were not yet fixed. Dawber Williamson Roofing Ltd sought the return of the slates, no payment having been made to them for the slates. The court held that Dawber Williamson Roofing Ltd was entitled to the slates, as there was no express provision in the sub-contract which would pass the property in the slates either to the main contractor or to the local authority. Consequently the usual assumptions applied, and Dawber Williamson Roofing Ltd was the owner of the slates.

(g) The consumption of the goods in a manufacturing process, or the incorporation of the goods into land or into the fabric of a building or other structure raises presumptions which will displace the previous rules and which will often displace even express provisions of the contract. This is true whether the contract in que∗ion is one of sale of goods or of work and materials.

In the case of *Re Yorkshire Joinery Co Ltd* (1967), a contractor contracted to supply its customer with materials to put up a factory. A condition in the contract provided that the property, both when on site and when put up, was to remain that of the contractor until it had been paid for. Payment had not been made, when the customer, a company, went into liquidation. The court held that once the factory had been built, and the materials fixed to it, the factory and materials became part of the freehold. Thus the contractor had lost title to the goods and materials (despite the express wording of the contract), and was left in the position of an unsecured creditor.

This and other similar cases raise important issues, and warnings for sellers and contractors. Unfortunately the reported judgments are not as comprehensive as one might wish, and do not provide the clearest of guidelines on which to base commercial decisions. The question of what is a fixture is sometimes clear, but can often be debatable, particularly where technology is concerned. Furthermore, it is not entirely clear from the reports whether the outcome of a case such as *Yorkshire Joinery* is dictated by a hard and fast rule, or whether it is a matter of the interpretation of the intentions of the parties. If it is the former, then *any* clause attempting to retain title in goods which become fixtures will be overridden at the point at which the goods actually do become fixtures. Whereas if it is a matter of presumed intentions of the parties, then it should not be beyond the ingenuity of some legal draftsman to create clauses which will make the sellers' intentions clear beyond any possible doubt, and to which effect will be given. As far as the *consumption of goods* in a manufacturing or similar process is concerned, the issue of title would appear to depend upon the intentions of the parties, rather than upon a hard and fast rule. In *Borden (UK) Ltd* v *Scottish Timber Products Ltd* (1979) it was held that where Borden (UK) Ltd sold resin to Scottish Timber Products Ltd, and retained title to the resin, that title was lost when the resin was used in the manufacturing process and ceased to exist as resin. The Court of Appeal was not prepared in this case to imply any term that the seller would have title to any new product made out of the resin. But two of the three judges of the court left it as an open question, whether or not the seller could have *expressed* such a term. In the case of *Re Peachdart Ltd* (1983) it was held that a seller lost title to leather (despite a clause retaining title) after delivery, as soon as it was worked on by the buyer, to manufacture new products. The judge stated that this appeared to be the intention of the parties. In reality, this particular interpretation of the relevant clause in the contract placed considerable strain upon the language of the contract, which clearly provided that the property was to be with and remain with the seller until payment had been made. If the issue is one of presumed intention, rather than the application of a definite rule, then the difficulties of convincing a court of one's intentions should not be underestimated.

RETENTION OF TITLE

Having examined the issue of title in some detail, we must now look at one of its most important modern practical applications, which is known as *retention of title*. Retention of title clauses (to be called ROT clauses in the remainder of this work) reflect the principle already discussed, which is that, in general, ownership passes when it is intended to pass. A clause in a contract postponing the passing of property to the buyer until the seller has been paid is therefore a perfectly legitimate expression of such an intention. The modern law in this area was tested and established in the famous case of *Aluminium Industrie Vaassen BV* v *Romalpa Aluminium Ltd* (1976), known more commonly as the *Romalpa* case. This case demonstrated that a suitable clause will prevent ownership in the goods of a particular contract from passing to the buyer until payment has been made, and will enable the seller to claim the return of the goods in the event of the failure of the buyer to pay. A well-drafted clause will also enable the seller to take other effective measures, such as claiming the proceeds of any of the goods which have been sold on to third parties while still in the ownership of the original seller.

We will now look at the issues under three headings, in order to evaluate the law and its practical implications. It should at all times be borne in mind that the law alone is not a sufficient guide to commercial judgments since such judgments must be made on a case to case basis by those involved in commerce, taking into account at least the following factors (and perhaps a number of others as well):

(a) the present state of the law
(b) the identity of the buyer
(c) the system of payment and credit
(d) the nature and destination of the goods, and what may happen to them
(e) the possible involvement of third parties.

The headings under which we will look at the issues are:
1 *Simple retention of title clauses, and the legal explanation of the principle.*
2 *More complicated clauses extending the rights of the seller and duties of the buyer.*
3 *The legal and practical problems of enforcing retention of title.*

1 Simple retention of title clauses

A simple retention of title clause is no more than a sentence or two declaring that the ownership of the goods which are to be delivered is to remain with the seller until a specified event has occurred. The event in question is usually stated to be the payment by the buyer in full for all the goods. In the *Romalpa* case, which involved deliveries of aluminium goods by *AIV*, a Dutch company, to Romalpa Ltd, an English company, the principle of this was tested. The Dutch company was owed in excess of £122,000 when a receiver of the buyer was appointed. AIV sought, among other things, the delivery up of the aluminium goods which had been supplied by them and which still remained on the premises of the buyer. Some of the goods in question had been sub-sold and delivered to third parties. The goods that remained were to the value of approximately £50,000. The court held that AIV was entitled to these goods.

A simple retention of title clause is just that, and nothing more. It is the expression by the parties to a contract of their will regarding the ownership of the actual goods, the subject of the contract of sale. It does not purport to deal with the consequences or the proceeds of sub-sales, nor does it purport to deal with goods which have been altered or consumed in a manufacturing process or which have become fixtures on land or premises. The reason why retention of title became an issue of great complexity after the *Romalpa* case, and the principal reason why it came to be described as a legal minefield, is that a number of sellers attempted to use simple ROT clauses for purposes for which they were not appropriate. Other sellers attempted to create more complicated clauses and came unstuck in their attempts to find the appropriate language in which to describe the obligations and relationships of the parties. Between 1979 and the end of 1984, in a number of important cases before the courts, the principle of retention of title suffered a number of reverses.

In *Re Bond Worth Ltd* (1979), the court held that the attempt by the seller to retain title failed; that the ownership of the goods had passed on delivery to the buyer, and that the clause merely created a *charge* on the property of the buyer, which was a company. A *charge* of the kind said by the court to have been created is *void* against the liquidator and any creditor of the company unless registered in the required manner. The problem after the *Bond Worth* case was, put bluntly, that the baby was in danger of being thrown out with the bathwater: we were aware that defective clauses might be construed as 'charges', and being unregistered, would fail; but we had not been given much guidance as to how to distinguish between a clause which amounted to a charge, and one which was a true and valid retention of title. The Companies Act 1948, and its successor, the Companies Act 1985, set out the law requiring registration of charges, in sections 95 of the 1948 Act, and section 395 and section 396 of its successor, the 1985 Act. But they do not enter into the refinements of the difference between retention of title and a charge. Not a few receivers and liquidators were able to seize upon this point, and to inform sellers who were awaiting the return of their goods, for which they had not been paid, that their ROT clauses were merely charges, and were therefore ineffective. This was the unhappy position until late in 1984, when the Court of Appeal, in *Clough Mill Ltd* v *Martin* (1984) at last set the record straight. In that case, a receiver had refused to allow the seller of goods (*Clough Mill Ltd*) to collect those goods from the premises of the buyer. The High Court had originally dismissed the claim of *Clough Mill Ltd*, on the ground that its ROT clause created a charge which was void for non-registration under the 1948 Act. In the Court of Appeal, this decision was reversed, and the ROT clause was held to be valid and effective. The Court stated:

'The concept of retention of title—or reservation of the right of disposal—pending payment of the price is, and has for many years been well known in commerce, as section 19(i) of the Sale of Goods Act 1979 clearly demonstrates ... the simple fact is that, under the first sentence of the condition, the buyer does not in fact confer a charge on his goods in favour of the seller: on the contrary the seller retains his title in his goods, for the purpose of providing himself with security. I can see no reason in law why a seller of goods should not adopt this course, and if the relevant contractual term is effective to achieve that result, I can see no reason why the law should not give effect to it in accordance with its terms.'

2 More complicated clauses extending the rights of the seller and the duties of the buyer

The *Clough Mill* case of 1984 was of enormous value to lawyers and to sellers of goods. Retention of title was confirmed as a legal possibility, particularly in cases in which standard claims for the return of the original goods delivered were made. But although the case contained fine and comprehensive judgments of the issues before the court, it did not and could not purport to resolve all the issues that could arise in very different circumstances which were not the subject of discussion in that case. To evaluate the impact of the *Clough Mill* decision we must consider a range of issues and the context in which they may arise.

Sellers of goods, when they use ROT clauses, are seeking a particular way of securing themselves against non-payment by their buyers: they intend to put themselves in a position where they can recover goods or their proceeds in the event of their buyer failing to pay. This may occur while the buyer is still solvent, or it may occur when the buyer is in receivership or liquidation or otherwise insolvent. The task of the seller, before making the contract, is to foresee all likely circumstances, and to decide how far he wishes to provide for them (as well as how far he is legally able to provide for them) in his conditions of sale. Now let us consider what the seller may wish to do:

(i) The seller may wish simply to recover his own goods in their original form. We have examined this in the previous pages, and have noted that it is possible to achieve this.

(ii) The seller may learn that his goods, after delivery to the buyer, were resold. The seller may wish to claim the proceeds of such resale.

(iii) The seller may discover that the goods delivered to his buyer have been incorporated into new objects (eg components incorporated into a machine, or substances used in a chemical process. The seller may wish either to recover his goods, or to claim some right over the new items or the proceeds of their sale.

(iv) The goods may have become fixed to or incorporated into a building or other structure fixed to land. The seller may wish to claim the return of his goods.

(v) The original goods sold may have been altered or re-worked or processed. The seller may wish to claim the return of the goods, or their proceeds if they are sold as new products.

The first of these issues was decided in the *Clough Mill* case. Each of the other issues has been the subject of at least one case either before the High Court, or before the Court of Appeal. It is not easy to evaluate these cases, because although none of them was overruled by the *Clough Mill* decision, it may yet be the case that the decisions were based at least partly upon assumptions which no longer hold good after *Clough Mill*. However, the following points may be extracted from the cases:

Proceeds of sub-sales

If a seller wishes to draft an ROT clause which keeps title to his goods until they are paid for, and which, in the event of a sub-sale by his purchaser, provides for the proceeds of such sub-sale to be held for his account, it is presumably possible to do so. We have authority for this from the *Romalpa* case itself, in which the seller, AIV, successfully claimed £35,000 representing the proceeds of sub-sales by Romalpa Ltd to its customers of materials supplied by and still owned by AIV. The court held that the third parties, who bought under the sub-sales, acquired title. This is because of the 'buyer in possession' rule discussed earlier. Romalpa Ltd may not have owned the goods, but it was able, as a buyer in possession, to pass title to sub-purchasers who bought in good faith in the ordinary course of business. However, in this instance, the court held that the proceeds were held by Romalpa in a *fiduciary capacity* for AIV.

It was implicit in the judgments of the *Romalpa* case that one must examine the relationships in each contract to see whether or not a fiduciary relationship has been created. In the *Romalpa* case, although the relevant conditions, which were a translation from the Dutch, were in some respects defective, the court was prepared to find that such a relationship existed. Thus the money was held for the account of AIV. If it had not been so held, the relationship would have been merely that of debtor and creditor, and AIV would have ranked as an unsecured creditor.

The absence of a fiduciary relationship: the case of Hendy Lennox Industrial Engines Ltd v Grahame Puttick Ltd (1983)

This case illustrates the fact that a simple ROT clause cannot be made to do the work of a more sophisticated one. In this case the clause in question, in the seller's terms of sale, stated:

> 'all goods ... shall be and remain the property of the sellers until the purchase price be paid.'

The buyer failed to pay, and subsequently went into receivership while the seller made claims totalling £33,282 against the buyer. The court held that the seller was entitled to the return of the goods delivered under the contract of sale. The ROT clause was effective in this respect. However, its effectiveness was, for practical purposes, virtually negligible, since, at the time in question, hardly any goods remained to be redelivered to the seller: all but one item had been sold to sub-purchasers in such a way that the sub-purchasers had acquired the property in the goods. Hendy Lennox Ltd therefore sought judgment for the *proceeds* of sub-sales. But the court held that the ROT clause in this case was inadequate to create a fiduciary relationship with respect to those proceeds, and thus the seller had no direct claim on the proceeds of sub-sales.

Manufacture, consumption, fixtures and fittings

We have already encountered this problem with respect to items which have become fixed to land or to buildings on land: the *Yorkshire Joinery* case. Obviously this is an area in which a seller of goods or materials, or a contractor, must review his system of payment with greatest care, since there is a strong chance that even an express ROT clause may be overridden. There is, however, room for argument as to what is or is not a fixture. Items piped, welded, or cemented into buildings or structures probably are fixtures. Items merely plugged in or otherwise detachable are probably not fixtures. There are bound to be many marginal cases, and an express provision entitling the seller to enter any land or premises to detach and recover the goods is in many cases desirable. In the *Hendy Lennox* case, the seller was entitled to recover one item (and was in fact awarded its value). This item was an engine which had been bolted into a generator. The court held that it was recoverable, since the bolts connecting it to the generators could be undone.

Where goods or materials *change*, in the process of manufacture or of being made into new objects or substances, the law is as yet uncertain. In *Borden (UK) Ltd* v *Scottish Timber Products Ltd* (1979), the seller had sold resin to be used in the manufacture of chipboard, and claimed to have rights in respect of the chipboard or its proceeds. This claim failed, but it could be argued that the reason for this was the inadequacy of the clause itself to address the issue. Lord Justice BRIDGE stated:

'The lesson to be learned from these conclusions is a simple one. If a seller of goods to a manufacturer, who knows that his goods are to be used in a manufacturing process before they are paid for, wishes to reserve to himself an effective security for the payment of the price, he cannot rely on a simple reservation of title clause such as that relied upon by BORDEN. If he wishes to acquire rights over the finished product, he can only do so by express contractual stipulation. We have seen an elaborate, and presumably effective, example of such a stipulation in Romalpa.'

The first two sentences of the above quotation cannot be argued with. The problem lies in interpreting the third and fourth sentences. We do not know what sort of express contractual stipulation Lord Justice BRIDGE had in mind, nor do we know whether or not other judges would be prepared to give effect to such a stipulation. In the subsequent review of the law given by the Court of Appeal in *Clough Mill Ltd* v *Martin* (1984), the three judges of the Court of Appeal took the view that stipulations of this kind would have to be read as creating a *charge*, which would then require registration under the Companies Act. This had also been the view of the judges of the *Bond Worth* case of 1979, and *Re Peachdart Ltd* (1983), which were cited in the case of *Clough Mill*. In the case of *Clough Mill*, there was indeed a sub-clause of the conditions of sale which stated that if any of the material was used to make other goods, the property in those goods would be with and remain with the seller until payment had been made. However, this part of the ROT clause was not strictly relevant to the claim before the court, since the claim was for the return of the *original* goods sold, and not for new products. The comments of the judges of the Court of Appeal, though helpful, are not strictly speaking binding upon future courts. Moreover, one of the three judges of the Court of Appeal, Lord Justice OLIVER, reached his conclusion that this clause created a charge with some reluctance, and said that he was not sure that he could see any reason in principle why the legal title in a newly manufactured article composed of materials belonging to A and B should not lie where A and B have agreed that it should lie.

In summary, this is a difficult and risky area, and we await a convincing judgment in favour of a seller before being able to advise sellers that they can create ROT over new products or their proceeds.

3 The legal and practical problems of enforcing retention of title

In this area of commerce, law is an essential part of the knowledge that those in business must possess. But a knowledge of the law is only half the battle; it is also essential to have a sound grasp of the practicalities, and to take steps accordingly. At this stage some important questions must be examined, concerning the contract and the administration involved.

THE CONTRACT

(i)   Do you want an ROT clause?
(ii) If yes, then simple, or extended?
(iii) Do you want to provide for any special rights or duties?
(iv) Check accuracy of expression, and complete consistency with remainder of the contract. Make sure that the final draft is approved by a qualified lawyer.

THE ADMINISTRATION

(i)   Check your system of negotiating contracts. Your terms of sale must be incorporated into the contract if the ROT is to be enforceable.
(ii) Evaluate your system of credit control. Remember that ROT is part of an effective system of credit control, but not a good substitute for it.
(iii) Assess the situation regarding your buyer and the ultimate destination of the goods. There is rather less risk (in most cases) in selling a machine to a factory as free-standing plant, than in selling goods which will be sold on, or manufactured or built into other items.
(iv) Keep effective records. Be prepared to produce the contract (in some cases this will consist of an order and acknowledgment), the conditions of contract, the delivery note(s), and the invoice(s).
(v)   Check your sources of information and speed of action, in case you need to recover goods. Needless to say, one must stay within the law.

It is not appropriate in a work of this nature to tell readers, whether buyers or sellers, how they should write their conditions of contract: so much depends upon who they are dealing with and in what context, and upon the commercial constraints that are put upon them. The object of this discussion has been to make those who buy and sell goods aware of the implications of the contracts that they enter into, and of the options that are open to them if they wish to take certain protective measures. Such measures are not always necessary, nor are they always possible, particularly if one is dealing with other parties who intend to drive an equally hard bargain of their own.

For those who do decide to take one of the ROT options, a knowledge of the law in this area should be invaluable in deciding upon which option to take, and how to arrange one's administration to optimise its effectiveness. There are further points that may be made here, regarding the application of legal principles. First of all, it must be said, with all due respect to the majority of lawyers, receivers and liquidators, that when the crisis comes, and a seller of goods wishes to recover goods, he should be prepared to back his claims with sound legal arguments. It has not been entirely unknown in the author's experience, for receivers, liquidators, or their lawyers, to raise arguments against the validity of ROT claims, which could not possibly be sustained, and which sellers have mistakenly accepted as being correct in law. There is no reason why a seller should accept an argument which is against his interests until he is entirely convinced that it is correct. Sellers are of course just as likely to be wrong as receivers or liquidators, but a seller who has an effective clause and a sound system of administration should at least be more confident of his ground than he might otherwise have been.

Identification of goods

One of the matters that might defeat a claim which would otherwise be successful is that of the identity of one's goods. It is not unreasonable for a receiver or liquidator to expect a seller to be able to prove that goods which he wishes to recover are the same goods that he in fact contracted to sell, and delivered to that buyer. In some instances the problem of identifying one's products is not a serious difficulty. In other instances it is, and those who sell such products should be under no illusions: until they find an effective method of identification, ROT will be for all practical purposes useless against an unwilling receiver or liquidator.

Where a number of transactions with the same buyer take place over a period of time, there may be the further complication of identifying which goods were the subject of which contract. Again, this matter should not be underestimated, since some receivers and liquidators have taken the point that the actual goods claimed by the seller may be goods which have been paid for, and should therefore not be handed back, even though money for other goods delivered by the seller may be outstanding. Legally the point cannot be faulted, since the seller does not have a general claim over the buyer's property, but only a claim to those goods the property in which has not passed. The seller will therefore be expected to show precisely which goods those are, for example by relating serial numbers of stock to invoices and delivery notes.

Some sellers have attempted to overcome this problem by a version of ROT clause which states that the ownership of the goods will remain with the seller until the buyer has paid *all that is owing to the seller*.

This kind of clause was in fact used successfully in the *Romalpa* case itself. At the present moment it has its advocates, and it is easy to see why this is so. For one thing, it can be argued that as long as *Romalpa* is law, a clause which approximates to that which the Court of Appeal gave effect to in that case must surely be a good thing. And secondly, if a buyer *does not own any* of the goods until the buyer has cleared his indebtedness to the seller, this should in a great many cases save the seller from difficulties in cases where he cannot serial mark his goods. *All* the goods should, in most cases, still belong to the seller. The seller should only have to show that the goods in question came from him and from no other seller.

However, a question mark still hangs over this issue. In the definitive authority, which is *Clough Mill* v *Martin*, the clause was not of this kind. It was a clause reserving title over the material only until that material had been paid for. Both cases came before the Court of Appeal. But *Clough Mill* v *Martin* is the stronger authority, because the *Romalpa* case turned upon a crucial *concession* that Romalpa was a *bailee* of unused aluminium goods, and for this reason other courts have had little difficulty in distinguishing the *Romalpa* case when they have thought fit to do so. In theory both kinds of ROT clause ought to be valid, since under the Sale of Goods Act the property in goods passes when the parties intend it to pass, and there should be no reason why they cannot decide between themselves, in the terms of the contract, what is to be the relevant event. However, in view of the ambiguity of the cases, particularly bearing in mind some of the decisions of the Scottish Courts, which have taken exception to clauses relating to debts other than the contract price, it may be wiser for the time being to stick to the kind of clause used in *Clough Mill* v *Martin*, although those who are unable under any circumstances to serial mark their goods may feel that the Romalpa style of wording will best serve their purposes. It cannot be repeated too often that these are precisely the kinds of issue that make ROT a legal minefield, and most definitely a 'spare wheel' rather than a first line of credit control.

The unexpected factor

Those who decide to sell goods on credit must assess the risks carefully. The risks will differ from trade to trade and from buyer to buyer. It is one thing to draft a contract which provides for the recovery of the goods, and another to anticipate the circumstances in which recovery may be necessary. Sellers should be careful not to tie their hands in this matter. Clauses should be written in such a way as not to prejudice a seller's rights under other clauses or under general principles of law such as the Sale of Goods Act or the common law. They should also be written in such a way that although the seller will have the right to recover the goods, this will *not* give the buyer an *option* to return them. The clause will usually provide, in addition, that until payment has been made in full the buyer will have an obligation to store the goods in such a way that they can clearly be identified as the property of the seller. As far as recovery of the goods is concerned, this may be necessary *before* payment has become overdue (because the seller is by now aware that when the time for payment comes, the buyer will not have the ability to pay). The clause should be drafted in such a way as to make this possible. The question of the *risk* in the goods should also be dealt with. The general principle that risk does not pass to the buyer until the property in the goods passes holds good unless the parties provide to the contrary. It is common for sellers who contract on ROT terms to provide that the risk in the goods will pass to the buyer on delivery, but there is no obligation to draft the contract in this way. The most probable advantage of placing the risk in the goods upon the buyer is that if the goods are lost or stolen or damaged, or perish, it is up to the buyer rather than the seller to make good the loss or damage. Occasionally the question has arisen as to whether or not the buyer's insurance will be adequate for these purposes, but this is another of the many factors that the seller will have to take into account.

One of the complications of the Sale of Goods Act 1979, is that under section 49(1), the property in the goods must have passed to the buyer before the seller may maintain an action for the price. If this is taken literally, then the seller who retained title in the goods would be unable to sue the buyer for the price, for the simple reason that the property would not yet have passed. However, under section 55 of the Act, where a right, duty or liability would arise under a contract of sale of goods by implication of law, it may (subject to the Unfair Contract Terms Act 1977) be negatived or varied by *express agreement,* so it is presumably possible for a seller to put a term into the contract entitling him to maintain an action for the price notwithstanding that the property in the goods has not yet passed to the buyer.

Next, as an illustration of the commercial complications which may arise, and of the fact that the law in this area does not stand still, we must look at the circumstances that arose in the case of *E. Pfeiffer Weinkellerei-Weineinkauf GmbH and Co* v *Arbuthnot Factors Ltd* (1987). In this case a German company sold wine to an English importer. The terms of the contract were those of the seller, and included an ROT clause, which was in a German original version, and in an English translation. The terms were expressly agreed between the parties. The ROT clause purported to deal with the proceeds of sub-sales in so far as it gave to the buyer permission to sub-sell the goods, provided that all claims and rights from the sub-sales were passed on to the seller. The goods were sub-sold by the buyer, on credit terms, and the buyer then entered into a *factoring agreement,* under which the debts owed by the sub-purchasers were assigned to Arbuthnot Factors Ltd.

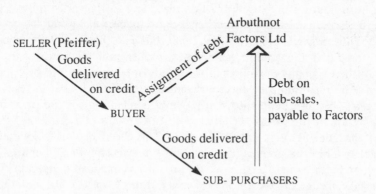

The question before the High Court was whether the title to the money derived from the sub-sales, and paid to Arbuthnot Factors Ltd under the factoring agreement, was with the seller or with the factors. The issue was tried as two preliminary issues of law, and judgment was given to Arbuthnot Factors Ltd, on the ground that the buyer had sold for his own account, and not as fiduciary, and that the rights given by the ROT clause, relating to proceeds of sub-sales, constituted a *charge* which was *void*, for lack of registration. The factors had priority over the interests of the sellers in relation to the proceeds which had been assigned to them. This case shows that *all* circumstances should be catered for and guarded against, and that translations of conditions should be either not used at all, or else reviewed most carefully for precision of language. Once again, the *fiduciary relationship* was a critical point at issue, and the wording of the clause in this case was held to be inconsistent with it.

RETENTION OF TITLE IN SCOTLAND

This work is primarily based upon English law, and it cannot be assumed that other legal systems follow the identical rules. Those wishing to know what the legal position would be in other countries should therefore consult works based on the laws of the appropriate country. Scots law differs on many issues from English law, and for the purposes of this area of the law, it may be noted that at the present time of writing the Scottish courts have taken a different approach to retention of title from that of the English courts. We have already noted that there is a difference between a retention of title clause which relates only to the price of the goods of the particular contract (we may refer to this as a 'price only' clause), and a retention of title clause that relates to all sums which are owing to the seller from the purchaser, on whatever account (we may refer to this as an 'all sums' clause). *Both* types of clause have been successful in the English courts. But in Scotland, a series of cases have taken a different view of the 'all sums' type of clause.

Basically, English and Scots law start from the same point of view, which is that the parties to a contract of sale of goods may, if they wish, state when the property in goods is to pass: section 17 of the Sale of Goods Act 1979. However, the Scottish courts will only apply this reasoning to the 'price only' type of clause. If the clause is an 'all sums' clause, it has been held that the clause is invalid. Thus in *Deutz Engines Ltd* v *Tepex Ltd and Another* (1983), where the clause stated that title would remain with the seller until 'all sums due from the buyer to the Company in respect of the goods or equipment sold or otherwise shall have been paid in full', the court refused to assist the seller in recovering the engines, because the clause went beyond a retention for the price of the goods, by use of the words 'or otherwise'. In the view of Lord Ross, section 62(4) of the Sale of Goods Act 1979 applied. This effectively ousts section 17 by stating that 'The provisions of this Act about contracts of sale do not apply to a transaction in the form of a contract of sale which is intended to operate by way of mortgage, pledge, charge, or other security.' Lord Ross took the view that the type of clause used was within section 62(4) as a form of security for sums over and above the purchase price. A similar view also appears in the case of *Emerald Stainless Steel Ltd* v *Southside Distribution Ltd* (1983), in which the return of goods to the sellers was refused on the ground that the clause in question went too far, in relating to 'all sums' owed by the customer to the seller, and was an attempt to create a security without possession of a type which was not recognised by Scots law.

This is the state of the law at the time of writing, and it is regretted that there should be differences of principle with regard to legislation which applies to both England and Scotland. Perhaps a definitive decision of the House of Lords will one day resolve the issue.

THE INSOLVENCY ACT 1986

This Act creates, among other things, a new form of order, known as an administration order, which may be made by a court in relation to a company. An administration order is an order directing that, during the period for which the order is in force, the affairs, business and property of the company shall be managed by a person (an 'administrator') appointed for the purpose by the court.

Normally, the circumstances in which a seller of goods may wish to enforce his rights against a buyer are: (a) if the buyer is a going concern, but simply has not paid its debts to the seller, or (b) if the buyer is bankrupt (in the case of individuals) or in receivership or liquidation (in the case of companies). Most of the cases cited on ROT have been cases involving a receivership or liquidation of a company which is the purchaser, although in *Pfeiffer Weinkellerei-Weineinkauf GmbH and Co* v *Arbuthnot Factors Ltd* (1987), the money was claimed from a factor rather than a receiver or liquidator.

However, when an *administration order* is made, there will be no receiver or liquidator, as long as the order is in force, although there could be a receivership or liquidation at some later date. The point of an administration order is to try, among other things, to keep the company as a going concern, and to have a more advantageous realisation of the company's assets than would exist in a winding up. Petitions for administration orders are made by directors or creditors of the company, to the court.

From the presentation of the petition to the making of the order, *no steps may be taken to repossess goods under any leasing or hire-purchase or retention of title agreement*, without leave of the court. Once the order is in force, a similar regime applies.

In the next few months, or years, we will no doubt learn more about how this works in practice. At present, it can be said that if an administration order is made, there is a risk that the seller will not be able to recover the goods when he wants to, although he may be able to recover them at a later stage, as long as they have not changed or otherwise become irrecoverable.

5 Terms about Quality

Contracts contain binding undertakings, and since terms about quality come into the ambit of such undertakings, those who make or handle contracts should always consider the precise implications of the specifications, documents, data, delivery requirements, and quality assurances that are to be given. It is usually at this point that references will be found, if at all, to those standards and descriptions and performance figures which might, if inadequately set out, easily become a matter of contention between the parties.

An undertaking, if given by one contracting party to the other, must be observed. To fail to do so is a breach of contract, and this may give rise to a right to reject goods or services as not being in accordance with the contract. Or it may give rise to a claim for damages, which could, in certain instances, exceed the price or replacement cost of the goods or services.

Before we make a detailed examination of the law, the following may be offered as a brief checklist of points relevant to this area:

(a) **Examine the specification** in every detail. Make sure that it is properly incorporated into the contract.

(b) **Read all documents** carefully. Make sure that they are consistent with one another. If any documents contain essential undertakings, make sure that they are referred to in and become part of the contract.

(c) **Check the full scope** of the contract: is it to supply goods, or to supply goods and documents and samples and spares, and lists, and permits and drawings (or any number of these)?

(d) **Define** accurately any standards to which an item is to comply, or any laws with which it is required to comply. Do not assume that such laws or standards (particularly in foreign countries) are automatically incorporated into the contract.

(e) **Check** the conditions of contract and other relevant documents to assess what kind of guarantee or warranty is given in respect of any goods or services.

Terms implied by statute

Having noted briefly that the parties to a contract may make known their requirements by *express* terms of the contract, we must now observe that the law also provides for certain terms to be *implied* into every contract. These terms are necessarily of a very general nature, but they do at least serve to ensure that certain minimum standards of quality are imported into contracts, even where the parties have not put these into express words. The relevant statutes are the *Sale of Goods Act 1979*, which implies terms into contracts for the sale of goods; the *Supply of Goods and Services Act 1982*, which implies similar terms into contracts of hire and contracts for labour and materials; and the *Supply of Goods (Implied Terms) Act 1973*, which implies similar terms into contracts of hire-purchase.

The Sale of Goods Act 1979 states that in *sales of goods by description* there is an implied condition that the goods will *correspond to description*. In sales of goods by *sample*, it is implied that the goods will *correspond to sample*.

Where goods are sold in the course of a business, it is implied that the goods shall be of *merchantable quality*. In general this means that goods must be of *acceptable* quality, that is, generally fit and free from defects, except in so far as the buyer knew or ought to have known (because of prior examination) of the defects. For example, in the case of *Rees Hough Ltd* v *Redland Reinforced Plastics Ltd* (1984), it was held by the court that concrete jacking pipes were not merchantable, since they cracked while being laid, and it was found on the evidence that they were unfit to be jacking pipes. This case is particularly important, because the specification of the pipes was, at least partly, included in a telephone conversation, and the court found it necessary to imply terms, as well as to rely upon what the parties had stated expressly. The case also involved terms of the seller which attempted to exclude liability, and as we shall see shortly, such exclusions of liability are not always effective.

Merchantable quality means that goods must be suitable for normal purposes, and this has recently been interpreted as meaning that goods must be suitable for one or more purposes for which they might reasonably be expected to be used, but that there is no requirement under this condition that goods should necessarily be suitable for *every* possible purpose for which such goods might be purchased. In *Aswan Engineering Establishment Co* v *Lupdine Ltd (Thurgar Bolle Ltd*, third party) (1986), this issue arose when plastic pails manufactured and supplied to Lupdine Ltd by Thurgar Bolle Ltd, and filled with waterproofing compound of Lupdine Ltd, collapsed. The compound, consisting of about 35,100 kg, was lost. The Court of Appeal held that the plastic pails were merchantable: they were capable of standing up to normal uses, and had been sent to many parts of the world without mishap. It was only the fact that they had been stacked in a particular way in exceptionally high temperatures, in the sun, in Kuwait, which had caused them to collapse. If a purchaser wishes to rely upon a condition in the contract that goods will be suitable for his own *special* requirements, the purchaser must satisfy the requirements of a different condition implied by the Sale of Goods Act 1979.

This next condition is that goods should be *reasonably fit for the purpose for which they are being bought*. However, it is only implied where the buyer makes known to the seller any particular purpose for which the goods are being bought, and even then, will not be implied in circumstances which show that the buyer does not rely upon the skill and judgment of the seller.

Information about the purchaser's requirements, and **reliance** upon some form of skill or judgment or expertise in the seller, are therefore the essential elements of this condition. In effect, we are asking whether or not 'performance warranties', or 'process warranties' or 'design responsibility' can be implied. In many contracts these matters are the subject of firm, written, express undertakings. But it is important to be aware that these undertakings can also be implied, from the extent to which the buyer has informed the seller of his special requirements, and the extent to which the buyer has relied upon the seller.

In the *Aswan Engineering* v *Lupdine Ltd* case mentioned above, a further issue that arose was whether or not Lupdine Ltd could claim that it had relied upon the skill and judgment of Thurgar Bolle Ltd to supply pails which would be suitable for its own peculiar requirements. The Court of Appeal held that it could not. Lupdine had made it known to Thurgar Bolle that it wanted the pails for export, but the evidence showed that Lupdine had made its own selection from a catalogue and a sample, and had not in any way relied upon Thurgar Bolle to specify a type of article which would perform under the conditions to which it was to be subjected.

On the other hand, in the case of *Independent Broadcasting Authority* and *EMI* v *BICC* (1980), the contractors EMI had contracted with the ITA for the supply and delivery of a television mast at Emley Moor, in Yorkshire. The quotation was for the *design*, supply and delivery of the mast. After being erected, the mast collapsed and fell, due to a combination of wind and icing, creating stresses as a result of an aerodynamic phenomenon known as *vortex shedding*. The issue was complicated by the fact that when EMI tendered to the ITA, the tender incorporated the design for the mast made by BICC (British Insulated Callender's Construction Company Ltd). The design had been prepared at the request of the ITA, and sent to them by BIC. The question was therefore whether or not EMI as contractor should bear a design responsibility in these circumstances.

The House of Lords held that on the facts, EMI did in fact take responsibility for the design. Most of the law lords put the decision on the basis that EMI was contractually liable to the ITA for the negligence of its sub-contractor BICC. But it was also accepted by two of the law lords that an undertaking as to fitness for the purpose of the ITA had been given by EMI. Lord SCARMAN stated: 'In the absence of any term (express or implied) negativing the obligation, one who contracts to design an article for a purpose made known to him undertakes that the design is reasonably fit for the purpose'. It should be noted that this case was not decided under the Sale of Goods Act, but under similar rules of the common law. These rules have now been put into statutory form in the Supply of Goods and Services Act 1982.

A case involving very different circumstances, and showing how far the principle of 'fitness for purpose' can be taken, is the case of *Wormell* v *RHM Agriculture (East) Ltd* (1985 and 1987). Although the buyer eventually lost this case on the facts of the issue, the case demonstrates that instructions and labels on goods can have a bearing upon their fitness for the purposes of the buyer. Here, the customer was a farmer, who claimed compensation for the cost of herbicide and labour in applying it to a crop of wheat. The goods had cost £6,438 and the application of the herbicide to the crop of wheat was intended to kill wild oats which were choking the main crop. The treatment was unsuccessful because the farmer applied the herbicide at the wrong time. This occurred because the farmer had read the manufacturer's instructions on the containers, and had drawn the inference that the herbicide would be of *some* effect at *any* stage, although there might be a risk to the wheat if it was used at a later stage.

Bearing this in mind, the farmer decided to take a risk. However, in reality, the herbicide was of no effect on the wild oats, due to its being used at too late a stage.

The trial judge held that the instructions were misleading, and awarded damages to the farmer on the basis that the goods were not fit for the purpose for which they were bought. The Court of Appeal later reversed this decision on the ground that the farmer ought not to have been misled by the instructions, and therefore the goods were not in fact unfit for the purpose for which they were bought. This reversal does not alter the broad principle of law, which is that labels and instructions are capable of affecting the fitness of goods for their purpose. It should also be noted that if the liability had been found to have existed, it would have been a *seller's* liability to the buyer, not a manufacturer's liability. In short, a seller gives implied terms about the goods he sells regardless of whether or not he is the manufacturer. See also *Hancock* v *B W Brazier (Anerley) Ltd* (1966): implied terms given by builder as to quality of materials.

Express guarantee and warranties

Apart from implied terms, contracts may also contain express undertakings. The expressions 'guarantee' and 'warranty' must always be looked at closely in their context, as they are capable of bearing a number of different meanings. A 'performance guarantee' given by a bank, for example, is quite different from an ordinary guarantee given by a seller as to the quality of his goods. Guarantee and warranty clauses in contracts may add to the potential liabilities of the seller, since the seller is giving undertakings in respect of the goods. However, they should be looked at most carefully by both parties since their impact differs greatly from contract to contract. Some guarantees and warranties do not in fact give a great deal to the purchaser which he does not have already: they are often little more than the equivalent of the purchaser's statutory rights. Some guarantees even give to the purchaser *less* than the statutory rights that the purchaser would normally have. On the other hand, there are guarantees and warranties which give to the purchaser *more* than the law would normally give by way of implied terms.

One useful way to evaluate a guarantee or warranty is to ask whether it is *in addition to* or *instead of* the statutory rights that one would normally have as a purchaser, and whether its overall effect is to give one *more* or *less* than one would normally have. These evaluations can be made by assessing:

(a) the *duration* of the guarantee;
(b) the *liability* undertaken by the seller;
(c) the *exclusions* or limits contained in it; and
(d) any conditions attached to it.

Exclusions of liability, or limits upon liability, or conditions attached to liability, are sometimes legitimate devices and therefore legally enforceable, and sometimes not. Since they are, in effect, all aimed at excluding liability which, but for the exclusion, the seller would have to bear, they are subject to strict canons of interpretation, as well as to statutory restrictions upon the extent to which they will be allowed. Limits upon, or exclusions of, or conditions placed upon liability must always be clear and unambiguous, otherwise it is open to the courts to place their own interpretation upon them. In some cases this will not be exactly what the seller of goods or services intended, but it will be what the seller was *presumed to have intended* because he did not make a different intention sufficiently clear. It is, for example, fairly common for contractors, or sellers of goods or services, to use clauses stating that they do not accept liability for 'consequential' loss or damage. The problem, not always sufficiently appreciated by those using such clauses, is that the word 'consequential' may mean a number of things to different people. Some sellers believe that a clause excluding liability for *consequential* loss or damage will protect them from *all* liability for loss or damage caused by late supply, or by defective goods. This belief is in most cases mistaken, since the word 'consequential' *isolates* a *type* of loss or damage, and gives it different treatment from other types of loss or damage. To *exclude* 'consequential' loss or damage is therefore, in most cases, to *accept* liability for other kinds of loss or damage which are *not* 'consequential'. The problem is then to decide how the division is to be made: thus

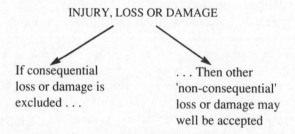

INJURY, LOSS OR DAMAGE

If consequential loss or damage is excluded . . .

. . . Then other 'non-consequential' loss or damage may well be accepted

This issue arose in the case of *Croudace Construction Ltd* v *Cawoods Concrete Products Ltd* (1978), in which part of a clause in a contract stated that the seller was not to be liable for 'any consequential loss or damage caused or arising by reason of late supply or any fault, failure or defect in any material or goods supplied by us'. The buyer claimed compensation from the seller on account of late delivery of masonry blocks. The lateness had resulted in a claim for extra payment by sub-contractors who were working for the buyer and had been kept idle due to the delay. The seller argued that there should be no liability on its part, because of the clause excluding liability for consequential loss. The Court of Appeal held that although consequential loss was excluded, the type of loss in this instance was non-consequential or 'direct' loss. The court said of the expression 'consequential': 'it may be difficult to be sure in some contexts precisely what it does mean'. The court then held that the seller had not excluded liability for the kind of loss to the buyer that had occurred in this case. It follows that those who wish to exclude or limit liability must be clear about what it is that they are excluding or limiting.

The Unfair Contract Terms Act 1977

A further difficulty that must be faced by sellers or contractors who wish to exclude or to limit their liability is that Parliament has found it necessary to place statutory limits upon the extent to which this may be done. This has been done in a number of different Acts of Parliament over the years, of which the latest version is the Unfair Contract Terms Act 1977. The Act was made necessary partly because of abuses of contract terms by sellers, particularly in cases involving consumers, and partly because of the tangled state that this area of the law had reached, due to attempts by judges in individual cases to find principles which redressed the balance in favour of buyers. The basic law is that the parties to a contract are just as free to reach their own bargain about liability or risks in relation to goods as they are free to bargain about terms of any other kind, such as price or delivery. However, because of the *Unfair Contract Terms Act*, certain types of contract term will not be enforced, and will in effect be treated as void. The Act is a most complex piece of legislation and it is not possible to examine all its implications in a work of this length, even if those implications were fully known, which they are not. However, the following summary is given:

Some clauses or terms attempting to exclude or limit liability are ineffective

These are those which

or

or

(a) attempt to limit or exclude liability for death or personal injury caused by negligence;

(b) attempt to limit or exclude the statutory rights of a person dealing as a consumer;

(c) attempt to exclude the implied undertakings as to title given by a seller or supplier of goods.

Furthermore, under the *Consumer Protection Act 1987*, which will be discussed in detail later on, it is *not possible* to limit or exclude the new **product liability** which arises under that Act.

Under the Unfair Contract Terms Act 1977, *some* terms attempting to limit or exclude liability are not entirely ineffective, but are only effective **to the extent that the term in question is reasonable**

These are those which

or

or

(a) attempt to limit or exclude liability for negligence *not* causing death or personal injury: for example, damage to property;

(b) attempt to limit or exclude the statutory rights of businesses;

(c) attempt to use standard conditions to exclude or limit liability generally, or to claim to be entitled to perform insufficiently or not at all.

73

The Unfair Contract Terms Act 1977 governs all United Kingdom contracts for the sale of goods, or supply of goods and services, or hire or hire-purchase. It does not, however, apply to genuine international supply contracts. Nor does it apply where foreign law is to be the proper law of the contract. But other jurisdictions may have similar principles, and the European Community has for some time been working towards a common system on unfair contract terms, which is expected to be in force by 1992. Meanwhile individual member states of the EEC have their own rules which correspond to some extent to those of the UK, regarding unfair contract terms.

Reasonableness

The Unfair Contract Terms Act 1977 gives to judges important powers to 'strike down' clauses excluding or limiting liability. Sometimes the clause in issue is struck down because the Act states that it is not to be effective. In other cases the clause in issue must be evaluated by the court, and whether or not it is to be effective will depend upon whether or not the court considers it to be reasonable. There have now been a number of cases on these matters. Simple comparisons are not particularly helpful, as each case depends upon its own special facts. However, a brief digest of cases may be given:

Phillips Products Ltd v *Hyland* (1984)
An excavator was hired to Phillips Products Ltd, and the owner provided both the machine and the driver. The contract was on the owner's standard conditions of hire, and a clause stated that the driver was to be regarded as being under the direction and control of the hirer and to be regarded as the servant or agent of the hirer. The driver negligently drove the equipment into the building of Phillips Products Ltd. The court held that *in this case* the clause in issue was *not* a fair one, and that the owner of the equipment was liable to the hirer for the driver's negligence.

The case of *Phillips Products Ltd* v *Hyland* does not mean that all such clauses are invalid: it simply means that they must be used with discretion, and that they *can* be ruled unfair. In *Thompson* v *T Lohan (Plant Hire) Ltd* (1987) the Court of Appeal allowed a similar clause to stand, and to protect the owner of hired industrial plant, but in very different circumstances to those of the first case.

Here, equipment was hired, together with a driver, who was, under the contract conditions, stated to be regarded as being the servant or agent of the hirer. The driver injured a *third party*, due to negligence. The court held that in this case the owner and the hirer had *agreed* that if a person was injured by negligence, it would be the hirer who would bear responsibility. The court distinguished *Phillips* v *Hyland* by stating that the former case was an *exclusion* of liability, which was unfair, whereas the present case involved an arrangement for *allocation* of liability as between owner and hirer, and did not affect the rights of the injured party and, accordingly, the condition was valid.

In *Rees Hough Ltd* v *Redland Reinforced Plastics Ltd* (1984), the facts of which have already been considered in this chapter, there was a clause in the conditions of sale of the seller, which stated that the seller would be liable only in respect of defects notified within three months of delivery of the goods. The same clause went on to exclude all other terms and conditions and liabilities under statute or otherwise, other than the undertakings expressly given in the warranty. The court held that this contractual clause did *not* satisfy the requirement of reasonableness.

In *Mitchell (George) Ltd* v *Finney Lock Seeds Ltd* (1983), the predecessor of the Unfair Contract Terms Act 1977 was tested in the House of Lords. In this case there had been a sale of seeds to a farming business, and a clause in the conditions of sale restricted liability to the price of the goods sold. In the event, the seeds grew into a virtually worthless product, and the farming business sued for damages. The seller relied on the restriction of liability, but the House of Lords held that in this particular case it would not be fair to allow the seller to escape liability, and accordingly the seller was liable for the full amount of the loss.

In analysing terms and conditions of contract, it is important to adopt the correct methodology. *Not all* conditions of contract are subject to the Unfair Contract Terms Act, or to the test of reasonableness. Thus, in a given set of circumstances we must ask:

(a) Is this contract governed by the Unfair Contract Terms Act 1977?
(b) Has one party become liable to the other under the contract or under the laws of negligence?
(c) Does the contract contain a term which attempts to exclude or to limit the liability of one party to the other for breach of contract or for negligence?
(d) Is that term ineffective in any circumstances, or is it subject to the test of reasonableness?
(e) If the latter, then is the term one which satisfies the requirements of reasonableness?

The test of reasonableness will be applied with regard to the wording of the clause of the contract which is in issue, as well as with regard to the clarity of the conditions, and the extent to which the clause is a negotiated one as opposed to one offered on a 'take it or leave it' basis. Of course, the *degree* of exclusion or of limitation of liability is highly relevant, as is evident from *Rees Hough Ltd* v *Redland Reinforced Plastics Ltd*, and from *Mitchell Ltd* v *Finney Lock Seeds Ltd*. The courts may well feel that it is reasonable for a seller to accept an amount of liability and to exclude the remainder, but the question still remains as to what that amount should be. Bearing in mind that the onus is on the party in breach to prove that the clause is a reasonable one, it is important to get this matter of judgment right, and to bear in mind that there is no all-purpose clause which will suit all circumstances.

Terms about quality: special considerations in relation to commercial contracts

Having outlined the law on the previous pages, we must of course be careful not to attempt to put all business contracts into a straitjacket. There are bound to be situations where very different considerations apply. In defence contracts, for example, a manufacturer of a ship or aircraft or submarine may accept only a very limited degree of liability for the performance or quality of the item after handover. This may be for a number of reasons, and can be legally justified. It may be, for example, that there are numerous items in the finished product for which the producer has *not* accepted a *design responsibility*. In such cases, provided that the contract is quite clear about this, the performance or suitability of those items for their intended function will rest upon some other party. This is *not* an exclusion of liability: it is a *definition* of the precise responsibilities that one manufacturer is willing to take on, and those responsibilities which must rest on other parties.

Furthermore, the maker of a final product does not always know, or have precise details of, the treatment to which the product is to be subjected. With consumer durables, the parameters of use do not vary greatly, so that it is not too difficult to quantify what a 'reasonable' warranty of the items should be. But for certain types of naval or military equipment, or industrial equipment, the range of uses may be infinitely more variable. In such cases it may not be unreasonable for a manufacturer to specify a relatively short period of time in which he will accept responsibility for the quality of an item, and then, in effect say to the buyer (ie another business, or government department) 'after this point you are on your own, as regards the performance of the item'. This would not exclude liability for death or personal injuries caused by negligence of the manufacturer, but in *White Cross Equipment Ltd* v *Farrell* (1982) it was held that a six month warranty of a waste compactor which was sold by one business to another, with an exclusion of liability thereafter, was not unreasonable, and was effective to prevent the seller being liable for the *performance* of the item after the six months had expired. Giving judgment, the judge stated that the case involved two businesses dealing as equals. The terms were clear. The warranty was a reasonable time within which defects ought to have emerged. Perhaps the most significant point was that the item in question, a waste compactor, was of the type which could be subjected to a variety of possible uses, and its life-span would presumably bear a relationship to the way in which the particular buyer used it.

Businesses dealing with private consumers

It must be emphasised that where a buyer buys or hires consumer goods or services from a business for his private use, the contract must *not* attempt to exclude or restrict the consumer's 'statutory rights'. These are the rights conferred on the consumer by the Sale of Goods Act, as well as certain other statutes such as the Supply of Goods and Services Act. Non-statutory undertakings in the contract can be restricted, to the extent that the restriction is reasonable. As it can amount to an offence to mislead a consumer about his statutory rights, most businesses which deal with consumers use a standard formula for their contracts with consumers stating that nothing in the contract affects their statutory rights.

The Consumer Protection Act 1987: 'product liability'

This Act, which will be the subject of more detailed discussion later in this work, brings in strict liability for death, personal injury, loss or damage to private property, caused by defective products. The liability is *not* absolute, since the defect must be shown to have *caused* the damage, but it is strict in the sense that the persons named under the Act, that is, *the producer*, the *importer into the European Community*, and the '*own-brander*', may be liable even without being to blame for the existence of the defect. This could occur, for example, where a bought-in component causes the defect in the finished product. Under this Act:

'The liability of a person by virtue of this Part to a person who has suffered damage caused wholly or partly by a defect in a product, or to a dependant or relative of such a person, *shall not be limited or excluded by any contract term, or by any notice or by any other provision.*'

It should be noted that this protection applies to the *consumer*. The problem for a business, is that when it buys in goods or services to go into an 'end-product', which will eventually reach the consumer, that business must rely upon *another set of rules* in order to protect itself against its supplier. The rules that it will rely upon are the laws of contract, such as the Sale of Goods Act, and the law of negligence. Thus the purchaser of goods and services should be prepared to:

(a) resist any contract with its suppliers under which recourse in cases involving product liability is difficult or non-existent;

(b) contest any seriously restrictive conditions of sale of its suppliers on the ground that the restrictions on the suppliers' liability are not reasonable. This line of argument may not, however, be available to those who buy goods from overseas, because the contract may not necessarily be subject to the Unfair Contract Terms Act.

Breach of the seller's undertakings about quality: the nature of liability under contract

In dealing with these matters we will assume that the terms of the contract do not impose their own regime upon the parties. Some contracts set out the remedies available to the parties in the event of a breach; if they do, then one would normally follow those terms provided that any *exclusions* of liability are reasonable. But apart from such terms, the law would give a buyer of defective goods the following rights and remedies:

1 Rejection

The buyer may reject the goods and refuse to pay the price, or recover the price if paid. Strictly speaking, there is no obligation on the buyer to accept replacement goods, although this is commonly done as a matter of commercial practice.

If the contract contains several items and one or more is defective, the buyer may reject the entire delivery. The only instance in which the law would compel the buyer to keep some goods and reject the rest is where the contract is 'severable' ie a contract for separate instalments to be paid for separately. Otherwise the *law* would require either acceptance or rejection of the whole of the contract goods. However, commercial practice often differs on this point, and many business concerns settle such matters in their own way. In the event of a failure to reach agreement on such points, it is as well to know how the law would be applied.

Time limits for rejection of goods

Contracts may contain time limits within which notice, or other action rejecting goods must be given to the seller. Such conditions will be valid, subject to the test of reasonableness in the Unfair Contract Terms Act 1977. There have been instances in which the time limits imposed by contract have been held to be too short to be fair and reasonable, and such time limits have not been enforceable. If no time limits are set down in the contract, then the law is that the buyer has a reasonable time in which to reject. This is not the same thing as a claim under a warranty, or a claim for *damages* for defective goods. What is in issue here is the right to *reject*. The law has, for a long time, recognised that if a buyer were to have an indefinite time in which to return goods to the seller, on the ground that those goods were not in conformity with the contract, then the seller might be put at a commercial disadvantage. Consequently, a buyer has every right to reject goods on the ground that they are either defective, or that they do not comply with description, or that they are unfit for the purpose specified, *but* the buyer must not delay unduly, or subject the goods to wear and tear or other processes which would make it commercially unfair to make the seller take the goods back. In the case of *Manifatture Tessile Laniera Wooltex* v *Ashley* (1979), it was held that a buyer which had waited almost four months before giving notice of rejection of a quantity of textiles was entitled to reject. In this case the contract did not provide a specific period for rejection, and the buyer had in fact given warning to the seller shortly after delivery, stating that some of the goods might not be of the right quality, and that rejection might take place. The next few weeks were used to obtain an expert's report, and to arrange a meeting. It was held that the buyer had acted within a reasonable time.

2 Damages

Rejection and damages are not mutually exclusive: a buyer may reject defective goods and still pursue a claim for damages, for example on the ground that he has not had the goods required in time. But damages can be sought without having to reject the goods. The goods may have been wholly or partly consumed, or may have been in service for some time before causing damage or may, since the defect came to light, have been altered or repaired. The basic principle is that *a buyer is entitled to be indemnified against any loss arising naturally, in the usual course of events from the breach*, or against any other loss which the parties had in mind at the time of the contract. Attempts to make this test into an exact science tend to be frustrating and the matter will only be explored briefly: what can be safely said is that there need be no relationship between the contract price of goods and the damages that can be claimed if they are unfit or defective.

Harbutt's Plasticine Ltd v *Wayne Tank and Pump Ltd* (1970)
Here, plant installed in an old mill which was used as a plasticine factory proved to be seriously defective. The plant had been intended to heat the materials used for making plasticine and to pump them into the factory. As it turned out, the pipes through which the material was pumped were liable to melt at the temperatures reached. A fire broke out and destroyed the mill. The owners rebuilt the factory according to a completely different, modern design. The owners then brought a claim against the contractors for breach of contract. The Court of Appeal held that the owners were entitled to the cost of building the new factory (*not* the value of the old factory, and *not* the value of the contract for plant). The new design, in this case, although different from the old, did no more than replace what was lost.

Parsons (Livestock) Ltd v *Uttley Ingham and Co Ltd* (1977)
Here a buyer contracted for a storage hopper 'with ventilated top and complete with filler and breather pipes'. It was delivered and installed, but had not been correctly adjusted so the ventilator did not work. This caused food poisoning to the livestock of the buyer, a farming concern, which had bought the hopper for food storage. The buyer was successful in a very substantial claim for the loss caused. The claim was *not* merely to have the hopper adjusted or replaced; nor was it merely a claim for the value of the animal food that was affected; it related to all the damage that arose naturally, in the ordinary course of things, and therefore included damages for loss of livestock.

'Consequential loss': we have already noted that this is not an easy concept to define, and there are a surprising number of versions of what it is supposed to mean. At this stage we may, however, ask whether or not 'consequential' damages, in the sense of loss of profits or production, may be recovered. The short answer is *yes, unless the contract excludes such damages*. A *reasonable* figure for profits or for inconvenience or loss of business may be recovered where the parties are well aware that goods or an installation are needed for the running of a business, and that losses will result from delays and/or defects.

The injured party must act reasonably, and take reasonable steps to reduce his loss. Ordinary profits, where lost, are normally recoverable. Special profits, etc, would only be recoverable if the seller had actual knowledge of the circumstances.

79

Victoria Laundry (Windsor) Ltd v *Newman Industries Ltd* (1949)

In this case the court allowed a buyer loss of profits due to the late delivery of a boiler. However, the loss was confined to ordinary profits that would have been earned through extension of the business, and to the *normal* rates of profits that would have been earned on certain dyeing contracts. Exceptionally high profits that would have been earned on those dyeing contracts were disallowed, since the seller did not know of them.

The general principle of restitution

One of the problems relating to breach of contract is the *measure* of the remedy available to the party suffering the breach. Suppose, for example, that a seller delivers defective goods to a buyer, as a result of which the buyer sustains damage to other plant or equipment of his. Should the buyer be compensated by the cost of a *new* piece of equipment, to replace the old, or by the *value* of the *old* piece of equipment at the time of its destruction? If the item can be repaired, the cost of repair is the correct measure. But what if it is completely destroyed? This issue arose in *Bacon* v *Cooper (Metals) Ltd* (1981), as well as in the *Harbutt's Plasticine* case.

In *Bacon* v *Cooper (Metals) Ltd* (1981), the plaintiff, Bacon, was a dealer in scrap metal. He had purchased a fragmentiser under a hire-purchase agreement. This machine was fitted with a rotor which, if properly maintained would be expected to last seven years. Bacon purchased steel from Cooper Metals Ltd, and fed the steel into the machine. The machine was damaged beyond repair, due to the quality of the steel, and it was found that the steel was not of the contract description, nor was it merchantable, nor fit for the purpose required.

The court found that rotors, unlike motor cars, were not bought and sold secondhand. They were used until worn out; there was no market in which one could go out and buy a partly used rotor. Consequently the judge awarded the plaintiff the full cost of a new rotor, as well as the extra hire-purchase charges that this involved. The basis of the decision is that the person suffering from a breach of contract is only bound to act reasonably. He does not have to take the steps which would cause the lowest costs to the person in breach of contract.

Apart from this principle of reasonableness, the general rule is that losses claimed must follow naturally from the breach of contract.

6 Liability without reliance upon a Contract: Negligence and Product Liability

The law of negligence

We must now begin to examine forms of liability where the person who suffers injury or loss is not claiming under a contract. There may be one or two basic reasons for this:

(i) because the injured party is not a party to any contract. He may, for example, be an employee of the purchaser, or the recipient of a gift;

(ii) because the injured party, although he has a contract, does not choose to base his claim upon his contract. This could be due to one of a number of possible factors, such as the fact that the seller with whom the contract existed has gone out of business; or it may be that the terms of the particular contract of sale are not very favourable to the buyer; or it may be that the buyer would prefer to by-pass the seller of a product and sue the *manufacturer*.

Whatever the reason, there may be many instances where the injured party will decide that he is better off relying upon a claim brought under the *laws of negligence* rather than on a claim brought under his contract. (Having stated this, it should nonetheless be recognised that the majority of claims, where a contractual relationship exists, will still be based on contract, because it tends to be easier to establish liability.)

The trend in English law has been to evolve gradually the right of one person to claim against another on account of negligence. Over a century ago it would have been very difficult indeed to claim against a manufacturer of a product unless one had entered into a contract with that manufacturer. So, for example, the driver of a coach, who was injured due to the collapse of a wheel of the coach, was not entitled in 1842 to bring a claim against the supplier of the coach. The driver was only an employee of the purchaser, and had no contract with the supplier.

But in 1932, in an historic decision which is still the basis of the modern law of negligence in England and Scotland, the House of Lords conceded that a claim could exist in negligence when brought by the buyer of a defective product. The action was brought in Scotland. A woman had partly consumed a bottle of ginger beer, and on proceeding to pour the remainder into a tumbler had noticed a decomposed snail emerging from the bottle. She became ill as a result.

She was not the buyer of the ginger beer, which had been served to her in a café, and had in any case been ordered by a friend. Nevertheless the House of Lords held that liability could exist in such circumstances. In one leading judgment in this case it was stated that:

> 'You must take reasonable care to avoid acts or omissions which you can reasonably foresee would be likely to injure your neighbour ... By Scots and English law alike a manufacturer of products, which he sells in such a form as to show that he intends them to reach the ultimate consumer in the form in which they left him with no possibility of intermediate examination, and with the knowledge that the absence of reasonable care in the preparation or putting up of the products will result in an injury to the consumer's life or property, owes a duty to the consumer to take that reasonable care.' (*Donoghue* v *Stevenson* (1932))

The most important attributes of this form of liability are:
  (i)   that the manufacturer or supplier must be in a position where he has a duty to take care to avoid doing something that might cause harm; this duty must be owed to the person bringing the claim;
 (ii)   that the possibility of harm occurring is reasonably foreseeable;
(iii)   that the manufacturer or contractor or supplier must have broken the duty to take reasonable care: that is, he must have acted negligently in producing the defective product or service;
 (iv)   that there must be injury, loss, or damage as a result of the negligent acts or omissions.

Muirhead v Industrial Tank Specialities Ltd and Others (1985)

In this case a wholesale fish merchant contracted to buy an installation consisting of a tank with pumps, so that he could keep lobsters alive for considerable periods, thus expanding his trade. Unfortunately, when lobsters were in the completed tank, the pumps which were necessary for the circulation of water began to cut out, causing loss of the stock of lobsters.

The problem lay in the nature of the electric motors in the pumps, which were unsuitable for the English voltage range: they were liable to cut out at the permissible top voltages, which could exceed 240 volts by as much as 6%.

In a case such as this, it is accepted that the customer normally has a claim against his main contractor: that is, the firm or company responsible for the installation. In fact, the fish merchant obtained judgment against the main contractor, but this remained unsatisfied, since the contractor went into liquidation.

The fish merchant therefore had to bring an action against some other party if he was to obtain compensation. The problem was that no other party had a contract with the merchant, so the action had to be brought under the law of negligence. As there was a chain of distribution involved in the particular pumps reaching their destination, it was important to select the right party (ie the party in breach of a duty of care), against whom to bring the claim.

In the end the claim succeeded against the manufacturer of the electric motors, in respect of some, although not all, of the loss and damage. The basis of the decision was that the manufacturers knew that the motors were to be used in pumps in the United Kingdom, to circulate water in the type of circumstances outlined. It followed that the manufacturer had a duty to take care to make sure that the pumps were suitable for use on the United Kingdom system, and according to the voltage range of that system.

THE 'DUTY OF CARE': TYPES OF LOSS

We saw in the previous chapter that under the law of *contract* a person who is in *breach of contract* may be bound to compensate the other party to the contract to the extent of all loss which flows naturally, in the ordinary course of things from the breach of contract, or which the parties may reasonably be supposed to have contemplated at the time of the contract. This can certainly include 'economic' or 'consequential' loss: see *Victoria Laundry* v *Newman Industries Ltd* (1949).

Where negligence is concerned, the principle of the need for a 'duty of care', and the principle that the possibility of loss or harm or damage must have been reasonably foreseeable, have the effect that not all claims in negligence for all types of loss will necessarily be allowed. We must at this point draw a distinction between *physical* loss or injury or damage (and any financial loss associated with it), and *purely economic loss*.

At present, in English law, there is little doubt that if a product is negligently manufactured or marketed, or if a service is negligently performed, and if injury, loss or damage is thereby suffered, and if *physical* damage or injury is present, the party which can be shown to have been negligent will be liable to pay compensation for the injury, loss or damage caused. For example, in the case of *Lambert (Lexmead)* v *Lewis* (1982), a defective coupling for a motor vehicle broke and caused physical injury resulting in death to a third party. It was found that the manufacturer, and the buyer of the coupling, had both been negligent. It was held that there was liability to pay compensation in respect of the injury, loss and damage.

However, a question which has arisen on many occasions is the extent to which a person found to be negligent is liable to compensate the injured party for *financial loss*.

In a sense, most types of loss are financial: if a builder negligently damages an adjoining building, the loss to the owner of the adjoining building can be called 'financial', in so far as it will require money to repair the damage. But this type of loss does not give rise to any serious difficulty in law, because it arises directly out of physical damage.

The type of loss which causes the difficulty is 'purely economic' loss, sometimes called *consequential loss* (although for reasons given in the previous chapter, that particular expression is best avoided, or at least, if not avoided, it is best to define what is meant by it). English law has only in recent decades begun to evolve a principle under which claims can be made for purely economic loss, such as loss of money, loss of business or loss of profits, *under the law of negligence*. In the case of *Hedley-Byrne* v *Heller*, the House of Lords, for

83

the first time, held that a person could be liable for economic loss caused to another due to negligent mis-statements. The particular case involved a financial inquiry about another party, and was not a building or engineering case, but it was reasonably clear from what was stated in the case that there could be liability in respect of economic loss brought about by negligently given advice or approvals or references. However, it always had to be established that a *duty of care existed*, in the sense that the person making the mis-statement knew or ought to have known that his statement would be acted upon by the other party.

In *Muirhead* v *Industrial Tank Specialities* (1985), the proceedings had originally been taken against the *contractor* by the customer. The contractor went into liquidation, so the proceedings were then taken, *in tort*, for *negligence*, against the *manufacturer*. The case which eventually reached the Court of Appeal was concerned with the types of loss or damage for which the manufacturer was to be liable to the customer. The structure of the relationships involved here is important, since it is to some extent this which decides whether or not there is a duty of care to avoid any particular type of loss as between one party and another.

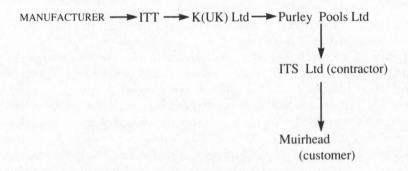

Bearing in mind these relationships, for the supply of the pumps, the claim by Muirhead against the manufacturer (ITS taking no further part in the proceedings) was as follows:

		£	
(a)	Cost of pumps	4,284.46	+ VAT
(b)	Labour in salvaging dead lobsters	500.00	
(c)	Cost of electrical engineers to attend pumps	500.00	
(d)	Additional labour	1,500.00	
(e)	Loss of interest on capital	to be quantified	
(f)	Loss of profit on intended sales	127,275.00	
(g)	Loss of lobsters at cost	11,000.00	

If the relationship had been one of contract, possibly *all* these heads of damage might have been awarded. One would have to look carefully at the actual contract to see what loss was excluded, if any. But in fact there was *no contract* between the fish merchant and the manufacturers of the motors of the pumps. In the event, the Court of Appeal allowed the heads of loss which related to *physical* damage in this case, but disallowed the claim for purely *economic* loss in this case.

By way of contrast, a few years earlier, the House of Lords did allow a claim for economic loss in the case of *Junior Books* v *The Veitchi Co* (1982). This case concerned the following relationships:

The claim concerned an allegation by the **employer** that the sub-contractor had been negligent in laying the floor of a factory. Since the employer was not in a contractual relationship with the sub-contractor, the action was in **tort**, not in contract. The case was a Scottish one, but it was accepted that there were no relevant distinctions to be made between the laws of England and Scotland on the matter before the court.

The issue before the House of Lords was not the facts of the dispute, but the *principle* of whether, even *if* negligence could be proved, the heads of damage were of the kind which could be awarded under the laws of negligence.

In this case, the problem lay in the fact that the defective floor was no more than 'defective': it had not actually injured anybody, nor was it a danger to any person or to any other part of the factory. It was simply a product that was not in good condition and not worth the price.

Presumably a claim could have been made against the **main contractor**, in contract, since there would have been breach of an implied term as to fitness or quality. But for reasons already discussed, the employer might have been unable or unwilling to bring such a claim. The report of the case does not enter into the reasons why the main contractor was not made the subject of a claim. All that we know is that the employer chose to sue the sub-contractor for what in English law is called *negligence* (in Scots law the expression is *delict*).

The House of Lords held that such a claim *could* be made. There was the requisite degree of proximity between the parties, and there were no good reasons for the court to restrict the duty to take care.

Points to note
1 All legal commentators are agreed that it is still too early to draw general conclusions from this case. One should not automatically assume that all customers can bring claims against manufacturers or sub-contractors for economic loss caused by negligence. All that can be said is that at present the climate is less unfavourable to this sort of claim that it once was.

2   The relationship between the employer (Junior Books) and the sub-contractor (Veitchi) was a particularly close one. The sub-contractor was a
nominated sub-contractor which had been chosen as a specialist by the
employer, with the employer relying upon the sub-contractor's skill and
experience. For reasons which will appear below, it may well be that in cases
where these factors are not present the courts will not allow that the duty of
care to avoid purely economic loss exists.

3   The claim was for damages for the estimated cost of relaying the floor
(£50,000), for the financial loss caused by having to remove machinery, for
storage costs, for loss of profit from temporary closure of the factory, and
for other expenses (£150,000 approximately).

The state of the law after Junior Books

The *Muirhead* case, already discussed, was a demonstration of the orthodox
principles of the law of negligence, particularly as applied to building and
engineering and associated commercial contracts. But its application to the
economic loss claimed in that case, as opposed to the physical damage suffered,
marks a process of retreat from what at first seemed to be a broader approach in
the *Junior Books* case. A recent decision of the Court of Appeal, also in a
building case, seems to confirm that the *Junior Books* decision is, for the
foreseeable future, going to be confined to a narrow range of circumstances and
relationships, and that it certainly does not mean that there is in any sense an
easy route towards successful actions in negligence against sub-contractors and
suppliers. In *Simaan General Contracting Co* v *Pilkington Glass Ltd* (1988), SGC
was main contractor on a project which required the installation of green glass
in a building. Pilkington Glass Ltd was not sub-contractor to the main
contractor, but was instead a supplier to the sub-contractor. Glass supplied by
Pilkington Glass Ltd was rejected by the architect due to discrepancies in its
colouring: it was of some importance that it should be uniformly green, whereas
it contained shades of red in places. The rejection of the glass caused economic
loss to the main contractor, which brought an action against Pilkington.
However, as can be seen, there was no contractual relationship between the
main contractor and Pilkington. As to the action in negligence, the problem
was, again, that what had occurred could be classified as *economic loss*, without
any physical damage, since the glass was not in any way dangerous or damaged,
nor did it cause any harm or damage. Here the Court of Appeal disallowed the
claim by the main contractor. The *Junior Books* case was distinguished from this
one, in that the employer had vetted and relied upon the flooring sub-contractor
in that case, whereas in the present case, although Pilkington were specified
suppliers, there had been no vetting of them, or negotiations with them by the
main contractor; consequently the element of reliance, which gives rise to the
duty of care in relation to economic loss, was not present in the case of
Pilkington.

PRODUCT LIABILITY: THE CONSUMER PROTECTION ACT 1987

The law relating to defects in goods or services is not to be found simply in one area of the law, but in a number of areas or branches of law which have grown up at different times. Third party claims for negligence grew up more recently than claims between parties to contracts. In the United States of America, a form of law known as *product liability* developed, under which third parties could successfully bring claims for injury sustained due to defective products, *even if they could not show that they had contracts, and even if they were unable to show negligence by the party whom they chose to sue.* What had to be shown was that the product was defective and that the party being sued was in some way responsible for the manufacture of the defective product or for putting it on the market. This development in the United States took place over the last few decades, and had no parallel in English or Scots law. However, new and important changes have recently taken place, and these affect all member states of the European Community, including the United Kingdom. The Consumer Protection Act 1987 was passed in order to give effect to the obligations of the United Kingdom as a member State of the European Community, and as a result, we now have 'product liability' in the whole of the United Kingdom. This has far reaching effects for the whole of industry and commerce: although the Act is called the *Consumer Protection Act*, the title does not, perhaps, reveal the full extent of its impact: there is nothing in the Act to limit its application to consumer goods or to items used by individuals in their capacity as consumers. The Act could in fact apply to *anything* that is capable of being described as a 'product', including ships, aircraft, and all kinds of building and industrial materials and equipment. It is therefore essential that all those who are involved in industry and commerce should be fully aware of the situations in which they (or their companies) could be exposed to product liability, and that they should take the necessary steps to lessen or to counteract this form of liability.

In this section of this work we will therefore be looking at:
(a) distinctions between the laws of contract, negligence, and product liability, including distinctions between the kinds of defect which may give rise to different forms of liability;
(b) the path to the new legislation;
(c) the content of the new legislation, its definitions, and the persons who may be liable for product liability;
(d) the defences which are available under the new legislation;
(e) the time limits for actions under the new legislation;
(f) some of the problems which are likely to be raised by the new legislation;
(g) the measures which purchasers and sellers may wish to take as a result of the new legislation.

Defects: different meanings: different branches of law
We tend to speak in general terms about defective products, but we must also recognise that different types of defect may fit into different legal classifications.

(a) A product may be **unsafe**. In this instance it is a 'defective' product in a

87

number of senses of the word, and there are a number of possible consequences. There may be liability under a *contract*, or there may be liability for *negligence*, or there may be liability under the new laws relating to *product liability* (the Consumer Protection Act 1987).

(b) A product may be *safe*, but *faulty* in some respect not affecting its safety. Here the seller may be liable to the buyer, for example under the Sale of Goods Act, but the new product liability will not apply.

(c) A product may be perfectly safe and perfectly made, but it may still be *the wrong product* for that buyer's particular requirements. This might have been said of the pipes in the *Rees Hough* case. Here, liability, if any (see the *Aswan Engineering* case, page 69), will be under a contract, but we must look carefully at the particular contract to see whether or not there is any liability at all.

The path to the new legislation

'Product liability' in the United Kingdom has always existed in the sense that there has always been some form of liability for defective products, firstly under contract, and subsequently under the law of negligence. But there were still gaps in the law, and the position of the person who has no contract and who cannot prove negligence was until recently somewhat weak. A new form of product liability was needed. Proposing the new Bill in 1986, Mr CHANNON, the Secretary of State said:

'This Bill will help us all get better value for money, by improving the design, quality and safety of products and also by improving the quality of information given to people before they buy.

By encouraging fair competition and the greater use of standards, it will provide an important stimulus for British industry to produce goods that are safer and of better design. This will lead to higher sales and more jobs.'

Mr CHANNON outlined the three main areas covered by the Bill:

– **product liability**, which will make it easier for people to obtain compensation when they are injured by unsafe products. In particular there will be strict liability; consumers will no longer have the heavy burden of proving that the manufacturer has been negligent.

– **consumer safety**, which provides a general safety requirement. It applies to all consumer goods and makes it an offence to sell goods that do not comply with the general safety requirement. It will enable enforcement officers to act speedily and decisively when dangerous new products appear on the market.

– **misleading prices**, introduces new provisions to improve and extend the protection against misleading price indications and comparisons.

Commenting on the product liability sections of the Bill, Mr CHANNON said:

'This will implement the European Community Directive on product liability, an important step in harmonising Community law. Manufacturers and consumers will benefit from having a similar regime throughout the Community, which will reduce barriers to trade. A common European regime, of which we will be part, will underline the quality of European goods and help us in export markets worldwide.'

On the general safety duty he added:

'Legislation on consumer safety already exists. But this works by giving powers to lay down specific regulations about particular types of products. This regime will continue.

'However there are shortcomings in this approach. It is necessarily slow because we must consult all concerned. There will always be gaps, since new types of product–especially novelty products which are all too often dangerous–continually appear. The general safety requirement will provide a much needed backstop to our consumer safety legislation.'
(*Source*: DTI Press Notice 20.11.86.)

We can now identify three different forms of liability: liability under the laws of contract, liability under the laws of negligence, and *strict liability* for damage caused by defective products. All three have existed for some time in the USA, but in the UK the third of these is the result of the Consumer Protection Act becoming law in 1988.

NB Although the Act was passed in 1987, it did not come into force immediately, and a period of grace was given. The Product Liability Sections came into force on 1 March 1988.

THE DIFFERENT TYPES OF LAW

If a product is defective, one must consider who, if anybody, is liable for it, and what the claimant will have to prove. These matters will depend upon the *form* of liability in question. For example, if a power tool is sold and proves to be defective, the following claims might take place:

(a) **A claim made under a contract**: this would be the normal form of claim between the buyer and the seller, particularly if the buyer is a business, and particularly if the buyer suffers no damage, but simply has on his hands a defective product. Under the contract the seller would be bound to repair or replace the product, or to provide a refund, and in some cases even to compensate the buyer. Obviously it is necessary to prove the existence of a contract (or of a manufacturer's guarantee). It is also necessary to show that the product really is defective, as opposed to wear and tear or misuse.

(b) **A claim made under the law of negligence**: this requires proof not only of a defect in the product, but also of negligence on the part of the person or company against which the claim is made. Negligence is not always easy to prove, so claims for negligence are not usually made if a claim could be made under a contract. However, there are cases where the claimant has *no* contract, or where the claimant is unable to use his rights under his contract. The *Muirhead* case, the facts of which are set out earlier in this work, is an example.

(c) A claim under the Consumer Protection Act 1987, or equivalent laws elsewhere eg the EEC, or the USA

This kind of claim requires *no* contract and *no* proof of negligence. It is made by a consumer who suffers *injury* or *damage* due to a *defective product*. The law has existed for some time in the USA, but exists in the UK as a result of the Consumer Protection Act coming into force. There will, of course, be subtle differences between the UK version of the law and that of the USA, as well as between EEC countries. But the essence of this form of liability is that the person injured is now able to make a claim *without having to show how the item came to be defective, or which of the persons concerned in its production or marketing was actually to blame.* The liability is 'strict' in the sense that as long as the damage can be attributed to the defective product, and as long as the person against whom the claim is made is a person whom the Act makes liable (ie a producer, importer into the EEC, or 'own brander', or in some cases a supplier), then the liability will be established. More will be said about this new law and its application and exceptions in due course. Now that it is in force, a person who receives a power tool as a gift, for example, will be able to claim against one or more of the above persons, without a contract or proof of negligence, if the tool is defective and injures him. For example, an *importer* into the EEC of the item will be liable, even though he is *not* in any respect negligent.

THE NEW PRODUCT LIABILITY
(Consumer Protection Act 1987)

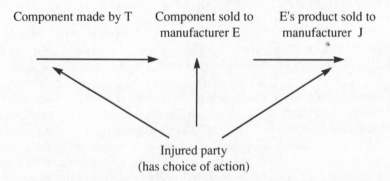

Component made by T   Component sold to   E's product sold to
manufacturer E   manufacturer J

Injured party
(has choice of action)

Under the Consumer Protection Act 1987, the injured party must be an individual suffering injury or damage to private property. He may claim against any producer, importer or 'own brander' of the product. The **product** includes all components and materials in it.

The company which **buys** a component, and which is sued for damages by an individual, may use its **contract** with the component manufacturer to 'pass back' liability. Failing this, it could use the laws of negligence.

Records   These can help with proof either way. There is no rule stating that it is fair or unfair to require them to be kept: it is a matter for negotiation between two contracting companies. However the closer a company is to the 'supply' to an individual, or to any situation in which an individual is injured, the more it will be likely to want records to help it to avoid or pass back liability.

Specific *regulations* may require that records are kept of certain types of goods for specified periods of time.

What are the implications of the new laws of Product Liability?

Although the relevant Act of Parliament is called the Consumer Protection Act 1987, no doubt because it contains other provisions related to the interests of consumers, other than Product Liability; the Product Liability sections will have repercussions throughout industry. They will affect the building industry, because building materials are 'products'. They will affect all industries concerned with, for example, the production, bottling, canning, packaging, etc, of food, drink, drugs, etc. They will concern the motor vehicle and clothing industries. But these are only the more obvious areas affected. In reality, *any* area of industry may be affected by the laws of Product Liability, and *all* areas of industry should prepare for these matters. A product does not have to be a consumer product to be the subject of product liability: a piece of machinery may injure a person, and this may give rise to product liability. Materials, components and all products which go into or become part of other products are themselves products for the purposes of this legislation, and may give rise to product liability. This means that, for example, all parts of metal producing or metal finishing industries are affected by these laws, because their products may go into or become part of other products, and, if defective, may cause the products into which they go to be defective.

THE CONSUMER PROTECTION ACT 1987

Part I of the Act creates the new dimension in UK Product Liability. It states:

Section 2(1):
'Subject to the following provisions of this Part, where any damage is caused wholly or partly by a defect in product, every person to whom subsection (2) below applies shall be liable for the damage'.

Section 2(2):
'This subsection applies to:
(a) the producer of the product;

(b) any person who, by putting his name on the product or using a trade mark or other distinguishing mark in relation to the product, has held himself out to be the producer of the product;

(c) any person who has imported the product into a member State from a place outside the member States in order, in the course of any business of his, to supply it to another.'

ANALYSIS

This adds an additional layer of liability to the laws already in existence, ie it does not alter the laws of contract or tort, but it does give the consumer an extra form of protection, in so far as the people nominated above (the producer, the 'own-brander', and the importer into the EEC) are now liable for the defective product irrespective of contract or negligence.

'Product' means any goods or electricity and includes a product which is comprised in another product, whether by virtue of being a component part or raw material or otherwise.

Buildings are not 'products', although materials for building are, and those who supply building materials, or parts of buildings, or building services and materials, are supplying 'products'.

Who is liable?

It will be noted that Section 2(2) places liability basically upon three classes of persons: 'producers', 'own-branders', and importers.

(a) *'Producers'*

In this legislation, producer means the *manufacturer*, and in the case of a substance which has not been manufactured, but has been won or abstracted, means the *person who won or abstracted it*, and in the case of a product which has neither been manufactured, nor won, nor abstracted, means the *person who has carried out the industrial or other process* to which its essential characteristics are attributable.

This last definition means that there can be producers of agricultural products, although at present the Act states that the liability in question shall not apply in respect of any defect in any game or agricultural produce if the only supply of the game or produce by a person to another was at a time when it had not undergone an industrial process.

(b) *'Own-branders'*

These are persons who put their own name or mark on a product and hold themselves out to be the producer of the product.

(c) *'Importers'*

These are those who import goods into the **community**. This part of the new legislation emphasises its EEC nature. An *Italian* company which imports electrical goods from the Far East, and then sells them in Italy to an English company, which then imports them into the UK, will be liable under this legislation. It follows from this that an *English* importer of goods into the EEC will probably be liable for the goods, under the corresponding laws of other member countries of the EEC.

Liability under this legislation is *not* confined to one person or company. It is possible for two or more persons to be liable. For example, the manufacturer of a final product, *and* the importer of a defective component in it may both be liable.

It will be seen from the previous pages that the proposed new legislation creates a totally new concept or dimension in liability, since the Act itself defines the persons who are to be liable, as compared with other branches of law which require either a contract, or else the tracing of the actual responsibility through negligence. It must be repeated that the other laws will still co-exist, so that, eg, a person who supplies primary agricultural produce may be liable under the laws of contract or negligence, even if not specifically caught by the new laws.

What is the position of the supplier?

If the classes of person mentioned in Section 2(2) are examined, it will be observed that they do *not* include the person who simply supplies a product, unless that person is *also* a producer, own-brander or importer as defined. Thus a person who does no more than supply, such as a retailer, is *not liable* under this part of the Act, *subject to an important qualification.*

This at first seems to protect an important class of businesses, but the following points must be kept in mind:

(a) Under Section 2(3), the supplier **can become liable**, if he is reasonably requested by the injured party to identify those primarily liable, and fails either to do this, or to identify his own supplier, within a reasonable time.

In short, the new legislation will channel liability towards producers, own-branders and importers, but expects suppliers to assist with the identification, or else to bear responsibility. Record keeping is important.

(b) Apart from the new legislation, a supplier will still bear potential liability under the law of contract (and sometimes under the law of negligence).

(c) The part of the new legislation which relates to **consumer safety** *does* apply to **suppliers**: *see Section 10* of the Act. This means that (subject to certain defences), the supplier of an unsafe consumer product *can* be found guilty of an offence.

What is a defect?

The important thing to remember about the new legislation on product liability is that it is basically a new branch of *consumer law*, although 'consumer' is not defined, and 'products' are not limited to consumer goods.

The liability is for *damage*. The *damage* is defined as death or personal injury or any loss of or damage to property, including land.

As regards the damage to or loss of *property*, it must be of a type ordinarily intended for *private use*, occupation or consumption, and intended by the person suffering the loss, mainly for that use.

As regards the damage done to property, it must be damage exceeding £275.

The defect must cause the damage: the liability must still therefore be established, as a question of cause and effect, although it will not be necessary to prove negligence.

As far as the meaning of the word *defect* is concerned, the Act states:

Section 3(1):

'Subject to the following provisions of this section, there is a defect in a product for the purposes of this Part if the safety of the product is not such as persons generally are entitled to expect: and for those purposes "safety" shall include safety in the context of risks of damage to property, as well as in the context of risks of death or personal injury.'

Thus the idea of a defect in this new legislation is *based upon safety*, and Section 3(2) takes into account:

(a) the manner in which a product is marketed, and any instructions that are given with it;

(b) the things which might reasonably be expected to be done with the product;

(c) the time when the producer supplied the product to another.

We noted earlier in this work the increasing importance of instructions with regard to liability, under contract law. This point is now taken up again under the new legislation.

Businesses should therefore review carefully the warnings and instructions and other labelling and marking of products which they produce, import into the Community, or brand as their own, with a view to effectiveness, legibility, accessibility, and durability.

The defences in the Act are that:

(a) the defect is attributable to compliance with any requirement imposed by or under any enactment or with any Community obligation;

(b) the person proceeded against did not at any time supply the product to another;

(c) the supplier was not in business (this presumably excludes liability under this legislation for sales by private individuals of secondhand goods);

(d) the defect did not exist in the product at the relevant time;

(e) the state of scientific and technical knowledge at the relevant time was not such that a producer of products of the same description as the product in question might be expected to have discovered the defect if it had existed in his products while they were under his control;

(f) the defect

(i) constituted a defect in a product ('the subsequent product') in which the product in question had been comprised, and

(ii) was wholly attributable to the design of the subsequent product or to compliance by the producer of the product in question with instructions given by the producer of the subsequent product.

As has already been mentioned, the liability under the new law will not be capable of being excluded or limited by any contract terms or other notices or provisions.

This basically means that once liability has occurred, no exclusion, etc, will be effective. On the other hand it does not mean that *warnings* are of no effect. On the contrary, warnings and instructions are of relevance in deciding whether or not a product is as safe as persons generally are entitled to expect.

Time limits   These are not the same as those discussed under the law of contract and the law of negligence. However, the provisions of the Act concerning time limits are exceedingly complex, and cater for a number of possible situations, so that at present the safest advice that can be given is that if a particular problem arises, detailed advice on this matter should be taken at that time from one's lawyer.

However, some general guidelines may be given, as these will assist with issues about *retention* of records and other information.

In general a person has three years from the date of the damage or of his knowledge of it, in which to bring his action.

However, the *three* years may begin some years after the supply of the product, so the Act imposes a *ten* year limit on claims, dating from the date of supply.

This means that it is advisable for businesses to keep records and information which will help them to defend an action for at least 10 years.

SOME PROBLEMS POSED BY THE CONSUMER PROTECTION ACT 1987

When a new body of law is imposed by statute, the statute is intended by the legislators to provide a framework within which questions which may arise have definite answers: there should be as much certainty as is possible in this kind of law, so that all concerned may draw the necessary conclusions about their obligations and liabilities, and may arrange their affairs accordingly. To a considerable extent, the new legislation achieves this objective. However, there are inevitably a few areas in which the complexities of modern industry and of manufacturing and marketing methods will cause problems of interpretation of the Consumer Protection Act 1987. The problem of the 'own-brander' is one such problem: one of the ways in which a person may become liable under the statute is if one is 'any person who, by putting his name on the product or using a trade mark or other distinguishing mark in relation to the product, has held himself out to be the producer of the product'. Clearly, if one states that one is the producer of a product, one may be liable for it even if one is not in fact the producer. But what if one merely puts one's name or mark on a product, *without* stating that one is the producer? Or what if a company puts its name on a product by stating that it is produced *for* the company named? Or what if a product bears a famous brand name, and states that it is produced under licence? Or what if *two* names appear on the product, and only one of these is the name of the actual producer? All these questions have been raised since the Act was passed, although at the time of writing this kind of question has not yet come before the courts. Until it does, the safest course of action is for a company or other business concern to assume that if its name is on a product, it may be held to be an 'own-brander' of the product. Businesses may then wish to consider the removal of their name from products which they do not make. However, some businesses will consider that the commercial advantages of having their name on certain products produced by others outweigh the risks of product liability. If this is the case, such businesses must keep their insurance under review. It may be (but has not yet been decided by any court) that if a business wishes to keep its name on a product, it may do so without liability as an own-brander as long as it states clearly who the real producer is; if this turns out to be the case, it may assist some businesses, although there will be other businesses which will be reluctant to reveal to all the world the identity of their suppliers.

A further issue, also concerning 'own-branding' arises in connection with complex industrial equipment which may contain many components. Each component may contain the name of its producer. However, it may be that the manufacturer which assembles the final product will find it necessary to put the label relevant to a particular component *near* to that component instead of *on* the component. What will be the position regarding 'own-branding' in such a case? Manufacturers of components may well decide that the safest thing is to insist that their name does not go onto any product other than the one which they have produced.

The expression *producer* at first sight seems to have been defined with some thoroughness in the legislation. However, a problem may arise where one business designs an item and gives another business exact instructions as to how to make it. If the second business then makes the item and sells it to the business which designed it, which then markets it, which party will then be the producer? Presumably the business which makes the item is a producer, because it is *the manufacturer*. The other company may or may not also be a *producer*, depending upon the extent to which by designing, labelling, packing, etc, it becomes involved in the manufacture of the item. Even if it is not a producer, the company which markets the product will presumably do so under its own name, and will therefore be an 'own-brander' of the item. In this kind of situation, both companies may have to accept from the start that each may bear product liability for the item; the companies may then arrange to regulate the risks between themselves by careful use of contract terms, indemnities, and insurance.

7 Performance

In order to secure the proper performance of obligations in a contract, the arrangements between the parties should be clear about what it is that is to be performed, and about the underlying principles upon which that performance is to be based. At first sight this may seem to be uncomplicated, and so it often is, in simple or minor contracts. But even in small contracts it is possible that one or other of the parties may make an incorrect assumption, and this can have a serious effect upon the position of that party, and upon the risks inherent in the project. In major contracts this is even more likely to be the case. Perhaps, therefore, we should approach the issues that follow in this chapter applying the famous mathematical principle known as *Occam's razor*, which is that one should make the smallest possible number of assumptions in explaining anything. It is, for example, unwise to make assumptions about any of the following matters, and instead, there should be clear contractual provisions concerning the question of:

(a) who is to be responsible for ascertaining site conditions or operating conditions or other conditions relevant to the performance of the subject matter of the contract;

(b) what is to happen if entirely unforeseen circumstances occur, such as subterranean faults, or rock;

(c) whether or not the contractor is undertaking a design responsibility, and if so, to what extent. Is he, in any area of the project, being engaged to achieve a given level of performance of the works or equipment, or is he only being engaged to provide an item specified by the employer, or to carry out the designs of another person?

(d) whether or not the employer is relying upon the skill and judgment of the contractor in the choice of materials for a project. This is of great importance in a project, particularly if suppliers of materials are nominated by the employer, or if the employer 'free-issues' goods or materials;

(e) whether work is to be done strictly to a written specification, or whether it is to be done wholly or partly to the satisfaction of another party, such as the employer or his engineer or architect. This issue can affect the question of whether or not the work can be said to have been performed, and thus it can affect the right of the contractor to payment;

(f) whether or not the employer or his representative is entitled to order 'variations' or 'changes' or 'extras' under a particular contract, and to what extent and under what conditions. Obviously this can make a significant difference to the potential scope of a contract, and to the contractor's obligations.

Examples

1 *Ibmac Ltd* v *Marshall Ltd* (1968)

This case was looked at in an earlier chapter, and is an example of the need for a contractor to check carefully the position concerning responsibility for site conditions. Surface water created difficulties for the contractor here, but this was held to be his responsibility, in the sense that under this contract it was for the contractor rather than the employer to check site conditions.

2 *Bacal Construction (Midlands) Ltd* v *Northampton Development Corporation* (1975)

In this case the employer provided borehole data to the contractor and the contractor's foundation designs were based on this. In fact the data was inaccurate in some areas, and the foundations had to be re-designed. Here it was held that the employer had impliedly warranted the data, and was liable to compensate the contractor.

3 *Cammell Laird* v *Manganese Bronze and Brass Co Ltd* (1934)

This case illustrates the fact that the question of who bears design responsibility, and to what extent depends upon the precise construction of the agreement between the parties. In this case the manufacturers of ships' propellers were specialists in this field. They contracted to make propellers for particular ships in accordance with drawings supplied by the shipbuilder. The drawings gave the dimensions of the propellers, but stated that the edges of the propellers were to be brought up to fine lines. One propeller, when put into use, created noise, which resulted in the ship failing a test. The cause of the noise was the finishing and shaping of the propeller. The court held that in this case the final finish and shaping of the propeller had been left to the skill and judgment of the manufacturer. The manufacturer was therefore in breach of contract. Section 14 of the Sale of Goods Act applied, and the seller was responsible for the fitness of the propeller for its purpose.

4 *Cable Ltd* v *Hutcherson Ltd* (1969)

Here the *tender* was for the *design*, supply and installation of a bulk storage and handling plant. The contractor prepared drawings relating to part of the plant, and the engineer required amendments to be made to them. The tender was accepted, and amended drawings approved, and a formal contract was agreed, under which the contractor was to 'execute and complete the work shown upon the contract drawings and described by or referred to in the specification and conditions'. Towards the end of the work it became apparent that this design would result in subsidence. The employer argued that the contractor bore responsibility for the design. The High Court of Australia held that because of the way in which this contract had been negotiated and written, it was only a contract to carry out the specified work in a workmanlike manner. The overall effect of the documents was that the conditions were paramount, and they did not provide for the contractor undertaking to achieve a specific result or level of performance of the works. This case illustrates the need to use an appropriate form of contract to place design responsibility where it is intended to rest.

5 *Steel Company of Canada* v *Willand Management Ltd* (1966)

This case concerned the issue of who was to take responsibility for the failure of a particular type of material which was used in a building project. The roofs of some buildings were to be covered by a steel deck, and to make this water tight, a membrane was to be used with a material to attach it to the steel deck. The material, a compound, proved unsatisfactory. The legal problem lay in the fact that the customer had specified the material, while the contractor had applied it and had guaranteed the roofs for five years. The court, in Canada, held that in this case the employer was entitled to recover from the contractor the cost of repairs which had to be done to the roofs. Although the employer had specified the material to be used, the contractor, by giving a guarantee that the work would remain weather tight for five years, had undertaken that the work would perform the function that it was intended to perform.

From these cases it will be clear that the parties to a contract may encounter difficulties unless they make clear the basis of the contract. This may be done by means of a written contract to carry out and complete certain work in a particular manner in accordance with certain conditions and in return for a price. The *contract* should state the *price* or the way in which it is to be calculated, and should refer to and incorporate the *conditions*, and should refer to all the other documents which describe the obligations of the contractor, such as the *specification* and *special conditions* and *technical and other requirements*. The conditions should also contain the necessary *cross-references*, and an *order of priority of documents* should be stated. The contract and the conditions should also contain clear *definitions*, since we have not yet arrived at the stage where words always bear the identical meaning in all contracts.

Definitions

These are for the contracting parties to agree upon, and obviously an exhaustive list of words or expressions which they may wish to define cannot be given here. A few examples are given, such as:

'acceptance'
'authorised person'
'contract'
'contract price'
'change order'
'engineer'
'firm price'
'fixed price'
'month'
'specification'
'sub-contractor'
'supplier'
'week'
'work'
'work site'

THE CONTRACTOR'S OBLIGATIONS

These should be described in the contract and in the conditions, together with the necessary references to the specification and other documents which describe obligations laid upon the contractor or work to be done by the contractor. Contracts vary widely in scope, and for the protection of both parties it should be quite clear whether or not the contractor is to be responsible for any or all of the following (which again are examples rather than an attempt at an exhaustive list of things which may be included in an engineering contract):

supply of goods and materials
labour
erection
testing
commissioning
supply of spares
supply of drawings
supply of instructions about operation, etc
maintenance
maintenance of supply of spares
protection of intellectual property rights
examination of site
compliance with special site or working conditions
preparation of documents
obtaining permits
insurance
providing services of consultants
co-ordinating work of other persons.

THE CONDITIONS

Again, these differ a great deal, and often *general conditions* are supplemented by *special conditions* for particular projects. The aim of a set of conditions is to set out those general terms and conditions which will govern the contract and the relationship between the parties. They will include terms about:

the contractor's duties
the employer's duties
assignment and sub-contracting
the site; inspection; access; security, etc
compliance with law
insurance
the authority of the architect or engineer or other persons
delivery of goods and materials
responsibility for goods and materials
allocation of risk; indemnities
title to goods and materials

patents and other intellectual property rights
confidential information
variations or changes
health and safety
time for completion, or a completion date
programme of work
progress; liquidated damages for delay
certification of work
payment, or schedule of payment
extension of time
inspection and testing
completion and acceptance
suspension of work
employer's rights to determine the contract
contractor's rights to determine the contract
guarantees and warranties
performance bonds or guarantees
law applicable to the contract
arbitration.

THE PURCHASER'S OBLIGATIONS

Just as a contract will always set out the contractor's obligations in some form or other, so a contract may also set out the obligations of the employer or purchaser. From a contractor's point of view it is most advisable that this should be done, since it serves two important objectives. In the first place it clarifies the question of who is responsible for what, with regard to matters such as access to a site, availability of equipment such as lifting equipment or tackle, the supply of power and water, the provision of the necessary conditions for tests to be made on site, questions relating to permits and licences, and a great many other matters. If these are set down clearly, this assists the contractor in the pricing of the contract work, since he knows the things for which he is to be responsible before he submits his quotation. It also helps to resolve any difficulties which may subsequently arise between the parties. Secondly, and following from the first point, if a matter is made an obligation of the purchaser, then a purchaser who fails in such an obligation is in breach of contract. This may involve the contractor in extra costs, and the contractor who can show that the employer or purchaser is in breach of his obligations may then be able to make a claim for an addition to the purchase price. Some contracts specifically make provision for this.

DISCREPANCIES AND ERRORS: DRAWINGS, etc

A building or engineering contract may be dependent upon drawings or diagrams to be provided by one party or the other. If so, then it is as well that

101

the contract should contain provisions upon this matter. Clearly the contract should make it clear who is to supply all or any of the drawings, etc: this could be the contractor, or the employer, or the engineer or architect. If drawings, and other similar information, are to be supplied by the *contractor*, and if an engineer or architect or other person is to be in charge of the project, then it is normal to require that the drawings, etc, are to be *approved* by the engineer, etc. The contract should preferably give a programme for submission and approval. There then arises the difficult question of responsibility for *discrepancies and errors* in the drawings, etc. If this is not dealt with clearly in the contract, it is not difficult to see how argument may arise: the contractor arguing that the engineer approved the drawings, and therefore being in the contractor's view responsible for the errors, and the engineer arguing the contrary. It is therefore advisable that the contract should contain firm provisions on this point. The Model Form of Conditions of Contract MF/1, 1988, of the Institution of Mechanical Engineers, The Institution of Electrical Engineers, and the Association of Consulting Engineers, contains a useful example of such provisions, placing responsibility for errors in drawings, etc, supplied by the contractor upon the contractor, notwithstanding approval by the engineer; it then places responsibility for errors in drawings supplied by the purchaser or engineer upon the purchaser. The contractor is not to be responsible for errors, etc, in his own drawings, etc, if they are due to incorrect drawings or information provided by the purchaser or engineer.

STANDARD FORMS OF CONTRACT

There are many standard forms of contract in use, depending upon the subject matter of the contract, the relationship between the parties, whether as employer/main contractor, main contractor/sub-contractor, or main contractor/nominated sub-contractor, and the other variables in a contract, such as whether it is for home contracts or for overseas contracts. Many large companies have their own standard forms of building or engineering contract for works to be carried out for them. Most companies which sell goods or services have their own standard conditions of sale. There are many institutions which have produced standard forms of building or engineering contracts, and these standard forms themselves run to a number of different versions and editions. The following is a list of some of the existing forms of building and engineering contracts:

The Institution of Chemical Engineers
   Model Form of Conditions of Contract for Process Plants. (Suitable for lump-sum contracts in the United Kingdom.)
The Institution of Electrical Engineers
The Institution of Mechanical Engineers
The Association of Consulting Engineers
   Model Form of General Conditions 'A' (1978, 1982) Home Contracts with Erection.

Model Form of General Conditions of Contract 'B3' (1971, 1980, 1982) Export Contracts with erection.

Model Form of General Conditions of Contract MF/1 (1988): Home or Overseas contracts with erection, and with special sections covering sub-contracts and electronics hardware and software.

The Joint Contracts Tribunal (JCT)

Standard Form of building contract (1963)

Standard Form of Building Contract (1980). The 1980 Edition has a number of variants, these being:

Local Authorities

with quantities

without quantities

with approximate quantities.

Private

with quantities

without quantities

with approximate quantities

Sub-contract documents issued by the JCT for use with the 1980 standard form of contract are:

NSC/1 Tender

NSC/2 and 2a Employer/Sub-contractor agreement

NSC/3 Nomination of Sub-contractor

NSC/4 and 4a JCT Nominated sub-contracts

Her Majesty's Stationery Office   GC/Works/1

General Conditions of Government Contracts for Building and Civil Engineering Works

HM Government   GC/Stores/1

Standard Conditions for Government Contracts for Purchase of Goods.

VARIATIONS

A contract consists of a promise to perform specified work or to carry out certain specified services, or to deliver specified goods, in return for a price or other reward. Whatever has been agreed is fixed and unalterable unless the contract provides to the contrary. Thus a customer normally has no right to change his requirements with regard to the specification or quantity of goods and services, or any other matters which have been set down in the contract as obligations of the contractor.

This, however, could cause considerable problems for customers in commercial contracts or in building or engineering contracts. There are a great many commercial reasons why a customer may wish to change his mind, and vary the scope of the contract or the work to be done under the contract. In long term projects the reasons why a contract may need to be varied are obvious: the unforeseen may arise, or newer and better ways of achieving objectives may be discovered, or errors may give rise to the need to depart from the original design or plan, or policy considerations may arise, for example in defence contracts, which may require a contract to be varied.

One way in which these objectives could be achieved would be for the parties to the contract to agree to discharge the contract, and to negotiate a new contract between themselves. This does occasionally happen, where no other way of re-arranging matters to suit the parties' mutual requirements exists. However, this is cumbersome, and would not suit the everyday needs of commercial contracts or ordinary building and engineering contracts. It is therefore common to include in contracts provisions for variations.

VARIATION, BREACH, WAIVER

These different concepts must be distinguished. A variation within the meaning of a terms of a contract dealing with variations is not a breach of contract: it is something foreseen by the contract and covered by the contract provisions concerned, and governed by the provisions of the contract generally. It may, depending upon what is allowed by the particular contract, come from the employer, or from the architect or engineer, or from some other site representative (although such persons tend only to be given a limited amount of authority, if at all), or even in some forms of contract from the contractor (a *contractor's variation*).

An attempt to change a contract which goes beyond the permits of a variation clause can only operate through a renegotiation of the contract, or through a *waiver*. If it is none of these things, then a *breach of contract* will be involved, since a departure from a contract which cannot be justified by one of the foregoing principles is a breach. A contractor who departs from the provisions of a contract without the legal right to do so cannot claim any extra payment. Thus a contractor who is required to perform certain functions at a certain price under a contract, and who chooses to perform slightly different work in a more expensive manner, cannot claim to be paid extra unless he has a variation order from an authorised person. The contractor is in fact in breach of contract. One cannot take advantage of one's own breach of contract, in normal circumstances: this point was decided by the House of Lords in *Alghussein Establishment* v *Eton College* (1988). The contract in question was a property development contract, and it was alleged that the plaintiffs had broken the contract, and that the contract should be terminated. The plaintiffs sought to keep the contract alive, so as to benefit under it. The House of Lords held that when construing a contract, it was to be presumed, where there existed no provision to the contrary, that it was not the intention that one party should be entitled to take advantage of his breach against the other party.

Either party to a contract may, however, *waive* his rights, or part of his rights under it. This is a common law principle, since the common law has long recognised that a party to a contract is entitled to indicate either expressly or impliedly that he gives up or alters his rights. It may be that a contractor begins to execute some work in a manner different from that provided for in the contract. If the employer is unaware of this, no waiver can arise. But if the employer is aware of this, *and* indicates to the contractor that the altered work will be acceptable, a waiver will arise, and the employer will then be unable at a later date to complain that the alteration of the work constituted a breach of contract. However, waiver is very much a matter of intention, and if a contractor wishes to rely upon a waiver by the employer, it is best to obtain evidence of this in writing. Taking over work, or even paying for goods or work, do not necessarily amount to a waiver of rights.

Waiver can arise in the context of *formalities*, such as the formalities required for a variation order. Most contracts require variation orders to be made in writing. Orders given orally cannot usually be relied upon. However, the employer may indicate to the contractor that an oral variation order given by himself or his engineer will be treated as valid. In such a case it may be held that the employer has *waived* the formalities, so that he will have to pay for the work so varied. This has been held to be the case in the USA.

Provisions about variations

Provisions in contracts concerning variations may be described in a number of ways. In some contracts the word 'variation' will be used. In others, particularly American forms of contract, the expression 'change' or 'change order' is more common. In other forms of contract expressions such as 'extras' may be used. As long as the meaning of the provisions is quite clear, the differences of expression are not particularly important. What is important is that there should be no doubt about the following matters:

(a)   what is comprehended by the expression used, whether 'variation' or 'change': does it include alterations to the work, additions, omissions, changes in working methods, and other types of changes?

(b)   who has the right to require variations or make 'change orders'? If it is the 'employer' or 'owner', *who* is or are the authorised representative(s) of the employer or owner?

(c)   what is or are the procedure(s) for variations or changes?

(d)   what rights of objection or refusal, if any, has the contractor?

(e)   how are prices and times for performing work affected by variations or changes? Within what time limits are adjustments to be made, and who is to make these adjustments?

(f)   how are differences of opinion to be resolved?

Rights of the employer

As has already been stated, without a provision for variation of the work, the employer has no right to require any variations or changes to be made. The point of having provisions in the contract is to confer this right upon the employer. Since it is the contract that confers the right, it follows that the precise nature and scope of that right will depend upon the wording of the relevant provisions. For example, if the provisions state (as they normally do) that variation orders must be made in *writing*, the contractor will be under no obligation to carry out the variation unless and until it is put into writing by the properly authorised person. This is a safeguard to the contractor, as he may then be able at the same time to obtain a written price for the varied work; even if it is not possible at that time to put a price upon the varied work, the contractor will at least have a written record of the nature and extent of the varied work required of him, and the person who gave the order.

The right to vary the *work* to be done under a contract, or the *order*, or the *specification*, means precisely that and no more: it does not mean the right to alter the terms and conditions of the contract. Furthermore, it means the right only to do those things which have been included in the contract as falling within the meaning of the expression 'variation' or 'change', or 'extras' or any other similar expression. It follows that if a contract contains a definition of any of these words or expressions, the definition must be studied. The definition is important to both parties, because it confers rights upon the employer, to require changes within that definition, and also because it means that if a particular instruction can be described by the contractor as a change or variation, then he can insist that it be put into writing with a commitment to pay for it.

Payment for variations

If there were no variation clause in the contract, or if an instruction fell outside the clause the contractor would *not* be able to assume that by complying with an instruction to alter the work he would be entitled to extra payment. The reason for this is that the employer might deny that the instruction came from an authorised person. The employer might even take the view that the varied work or goods ordered were a departure from the work or goods contracted for, and might argue this was a *breach of contract*. No contractor wishes to put himself in breach of contract, and consequently a variation clause is a safeguard, since it will give the contractor a means of identifying what is a proper instruction to vary the work, as distinct from one which is not.

The effect of a variation order upon the matter of price and payment depends a great deal upon the nature of the contract. No assumptions should be made about this and the provisions must be carefully scrutinised *before* the contract is agreed, particularly from the point of view of the contractor, who will not wish to agree to a contract which entitles the employer to vary the work without a fair and sufficient means of rewarding the contractor for undertaking the varied work. Not every variation necessarily results in extra expense to the contractor, and the effect of a particular variation in a particular contract may be that the price is unchanged or even revised *downwards*. The important thing is to have clear and workable provisions for dealing with the effect of a variation upon the price. It is for the parties to agree upon the adjustment mechanism which is most suitable for them. This might in some cases mean that variations will require *quotations or estimates* showing the effect upon the contract price, and when the order is issued it may include the necessary adjustments. In other cases it may be more convenient to provide that variation orders may be made, and the effect upon the price may be calculated at a later stage, either in accordance with a formula, or in accordance with fair and reasonable rates, or in accordance with rates or prices provided in a bill of quantities.

Effect of variations on the programme of completion

A variation order may affect the progress of the work, or the time within which it can be achieved, and there should be a means of adjusting the programme of work and scheduled completion date to take account of the effect of variations. This will be of benefit to the contractor, who will know the programme within which he is expected to work, and how this has been affected by the variation order. It will also be of benefit to the employer, who would otherwise have invalidated the programme or completion date, by ordering extra or different work, and who would therefore have difficulty in enforcing delivery or completion within the desired time. If the contract permits variations, and if it provides for adjusting the programme of work or completion date, the employer will have the benefit of the substituted programme or completion date, and will therefore be able to enforce the performance of the contractor's obligations within the time limits.

The scope of variations or change orders

A contract may permit variations without any express limits on the rights of the employer to order such variations. This is the case in many building contracts, and in government contracts such as defence contracts, where, in a major project, hundreds of different variation orders may be given. Here the only limits on the right of the employer to order variations are *implied limits*, such as those limits which are implicit in the definition of the word variation, or in the scope of the work, and in practice these implied limits are seldom invoked. Nor is there any reason to invoke any limits on the right of the employer to order a variation, as long as the contractor is willing to undertake the work and is satisfied that the contract provides for a fair reward for his efforts. On the other hand there have occasionally been cases which have shown the reasons why some limits on the right to order a variation must necessarily be implied. In Australia, cases such as *Carr* v *J A Berriman Pty Ltd* (1953) have shown that if a variation clause confers upon the employer or his representative a power to order work to be omitted, this power will not be construed so as to empower the employer or his representative to direct that part of the work should be taken from the contractor and handed over to another contractor. Closer to home, the case of *Sir Lindsay Parkinson and Co Ltd* v *Commissioners of Works* (1950) demonstrated that one reason why a contractor might wish to limit the right of an employer to order extras or variations is that the system of pricing may provide an unsatisfactory reward, or indeed no reward at all, for the contractor. In this particular case the contract was such that the profit to the contractor could not in any circumstances exceed £300,000. The Court of Appeal stated that if the contract with its variation clause was to be read literally, it would seem that the position was that after the contractor had earned his £300,000 profit he could be compelled to labour without reward or limit on any further extras which the commissioners might elect to exact from him 'till the last syllable of recorded time'. This was something which the Court of Appeal was not prepared to allow, and it was held that the basis of the contract was that the commissioners could only require work by way of extras which was not materially in excess of the sum contemplated in the contract, which was £5,000,000. Any extras above this sum would fall outside the contract, and would have to be paid for at reasonable rates. This case does *not* of course mean that *any* departures from estimates in a 'cost-plus' contract must be paid for as being outside the contract. The principle is that there are implied limits to the quantity or quality of work that can be required as variations or extras, and that anything which goes beyond these limits is outside the contract, and therefore the subject of fresh negotiations or pricing arrangements.

A similar position was reached in the Canadian case of *Cana Construction Co Ltd* v *The Queen* (1973). In this case there had been a tender for the construction of a postal terminal. The main contractor was required to enter into a subcontract for the supply and installation of mail handling equipment, and the tender was to include a figure for supervision and overheads and profit on this installation of handling equipment, on the basis that the estimate for the supply and installation of the equipment was approximately $1,150,000. In the event, the contractor was instructed by way of a 'change' to place an order for handling equipment above the sum of $2,000,000. The main contractor submitted a request for the 'change' to include an increase in his own payment. If this had been an ordinary change order, the pricing system would not have allowed for an increase in the main contractor's payment. However, the Supreme Court of Canada applied the *Parkinson* case, and stated that the order for equipment went beyond what had been contemplated by either party, and therefore was different from the original contract, so that a different sum had to be paid for overheads and profit.

We have now reached a position where we can see that work ordered under a contract can be placed in one of several categories: it may be something which the contractor is already bound by the contract to do, in which case the order is no more than an order to proceed with the work, or to comply with the contract or specification, or to do something necessarily to be inferred from the contract, or any plan or specification. This is not a change or variation. Next we have those orders which *are* changes or variations within the meaning of the contract and the expressed or implied limits. And finally, we have those orders which go beyond any express or implied limits, and which may be the subject of fresh negotiations and/or extra payment, or which, if they involve a serious reduction, the contractor may refuse to allow. This may be shown in a diagram: see facing page.

Express limits

These are perhaps less common in contracts than they once were, but it is possible to include in a contract a provision for variations with the qualification that the contractor may object to a variation order which exceeds certain limits, or which, together with such other variations as have been required, exceeds

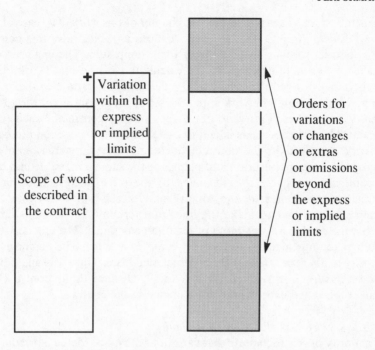

certain limits. The limits are usually expressed as an increase or decrease in the contract price of a certain percentage, such as 10% or 15% or 20%. In some contracts, the *customer*, as well as the contractor, may refuse to be bound by variation orders beyond the prescribed limits.

When is a variation not a variation?

There are at least three instances when an order will not be construed as a variation, and the employer may be able to avoid liability to pay an additional sum occasioned by an order.

1   Orders to do work which the contractor is already bound to do
These normally do not cause problems, since the contractor normally will be aware of the status of the instruction, and will not expect extra time or payment. However, the problem may arise if the contractor is under the impression that an order amounts to a variation, and the employer takes a different view. Or the problem may even arise if *both* parties are under the belief that what is being asked for is a variation, and the employer later changes his mind about this and declines to pay extra. The legal position is that if the contractor is already bound, on the true construction of the contract and any specification or plans or drawings in the contract, then he must do the work for the contract price, and there will be no duty on the employer to pay extra. Even if the employer gave a promise to pay extra, this promise will not be enforceable (except in some rather exceptional cases where written orders are treated as conclusive), because there will be no *consideration* for the promise to pay extra. The doctrine of

consideration was discussed in the first chapter of this work. The case of *Sharpe* v *Sao Paulo Railway Co* (1873), in the last century, illustrates this point. This was a contract to construct a railway for a lump sum. The engineer made a mistake of two million yards in the calculation of the earthwork. He then promised the contractor that he would make other alterations in the line, so as to diminish the amount of work required, and save the contractor the additional expense. These alterations were not made, and the contractor sued for extra payment. The Court of Appeal held that the contractor was bound to complete the work described in the contract, including everything reasonably to be inferred from the specification and plans, for the sum specified. It had been for the contractor to judge the adequacy of the price, before agreeing to the contract, and the contractor should have made calculations over again: this was a lump sum contract to make the line from terminus to terminus complete, whether the earthwork was more or less than envisaged. The engineer had not wilfully made miscalculations to deceive the contractor. The engineer had no authority to alter the terms of the contract, and his promise was unenforceable. As *Lord Justice* JAMES stated: 'it is a totally distinct thing from a claim to payment for actual extra works not included in the contract'.

2 Orders which lack the required formality

The majority of contracts state that variations must be ordered in *writing*. There is no common law rule about this, and if it were not provided for in the contract there would be no requirement of writing. The reason why most contracts do require writing is because without a clear record of what was ordered, and when, and by whom, and for what price, the matter can become very contentious. The precise nature of the requirement of writing will depend upon the form of contract that is used: some contracts simply state that a written order from the person authorised is required; other contracts go further into the *form* that that written order must take. Whatever formalities are required under the contract must be complied with if the order is to be treated as a genuine variation, with the consequent duty of the employer to pay. Sketches and certificates have, in particular cases, been held not to amount to written orders for variations. If writing is made a requirement for a variation, it does not follow that all written orders are then automatically variations: the test of what is already included in the contract is still relevant. One of the problems which may arise in this area is where an architect or engineer is asked to put an order into writing in the form of a variation, and he refuses to do so on the ground that it is not a variation and therefore does not require a written order. This type of situation could result in the contractor having to take risks, or it could result in delays while the parties continue discussions. An arbitration clause in sufficiently wide terms may help to resolve the matter, since the arbitrator would then be empowered either to give a ruling as to the legal position, or to award payment if the work were to go ahead provisionally with each party reserving his position. In the case of *Brodie* v *Cardiff Corporation* (1919), which concerned the construction of a reservoir, this issue arose, and the House of Lords held that under the particular contract the arbitration clause enabled the arbitrator to award payment for extras notwithstanding that the orders had not been put into writing as required by the contract. From this case it will be understood that the absence of writing is not necessarily fatal to a claim by the contractor for payment. Furthermore, if an order which is not in writing can be construed as a *separate contract*, then there is no reason why it should not be valid, since we saw in the first chapter of this work that a contract does not necessarily have to be in writing. Apart from this there have also been cases where it has been held that on the proper construction of the wording of the relevant clause, the rendering of a variation order into writing was not a condition precedent to *payment*, although it was a condition precedent to the contractor's obligation to do the work. In other words the requirement of writing was for the benefit of the contractor rather than for the benefit of the employer. Finally, there have also been cases where it has, in the particular circumstances, been held to be a fraud by the employer against the contractor to try to escape payment on the ground of the absence of writing. As a court will not wish to construe a contract so as to attribute fraud to an employer, it will, in cases of this kind, construe matters so as to avoid such a conclusion. For example, if an employer orally orders goods or materials or work, and is told that they will be extras, and if the employer orally confirms the order and at the same time gives the contractor to understand that payment will be made, it will be open to a court to hold that the requirement of writing has been waived. Everything would depend upon the view which a court might take of the circumstances and the conduct of the parties.

3 Orders made without authority

A provision for variations in a contract will entitle an employer or his authorised representative to order varied or additional work, or omissions of work. But the variation must be made by an authorised person otherwise it will constitute a departure from the contract for which the employer will not have to pay, and which he will be entitled to repudiate.

The question of authority will depend upon what is stated in the contract. In some contracts the provisions regarding variations will confer authority upon the architect or the engineer. This is because the employer may wish all such decisions to be made by the architect or engineer. The architect or engineer may lack any *implied* or *ostensible* authority to contract on behalf of the employer or to vary the work. But a provision giving the architect or engineer *express* authority establishes his authority in the eyes of the contractor, who will then know from whom to take his instructions. Some contracts do not mention an architect or engineer, but instead refer to an authorised representative, in which case it is most important to establish who is the relevant authorised representative. If there are express provisions on this point, such as a schedule or clause in the contract naming each person who is entitled to represent the employer, and stating his capacity or function, then these provisions should be adhered to. Problems may arise where such provisions are lacking. This raises the legal question of authority generally. This is a far wider issue of law than the issue of variations, and it will be discussed in the next few paragraphs.

AUTHORITY

The majority of purchasers in commercial contracts, or in building and engineering contracts, are probably corporations in the sense that they are likely to be companies, local authorities, or other public bodies. Corporations are inanimate beings and can only do the things which individuals may do through their agents: there must at some point be human beings who can act for and on behalf of the corporation. Individuals, too, may appoint agents. In transactions of the kind discussed in this work, agents may be involved in the negotiation of the contract, in the formation of the contract, in the performance of duties under the contract, such as delivery or shipping, in the initiation of changes, in the granting of extensions of time, in the approval or certification of work, in the carrying out of tests or inspections, and in the authorisation of payment, as well as in the general supervision of the contract. An agent, for these purposes, is any person authorised to carry out the function in question, and it is often the case in major projects that different persons carry out different functions, although it may also be the case that a single person is in charge of the whole project, as the 'architect' or the 'engineer', and may carry out most of these functions, other than the making of the contract itself. One cannot generalise because much will depend upon the internal structure of the corporation, and upon the question of whether, in a particular project, it is relying upon its own employees or upon the services of outside agents.

One person may only represent another to the extent that he has *authority* to do so. This authority is normally created by the employer in his contractual relationship with the agent (who is often an employee), and then conveyed to the contractor by means of the commercial or building or engineering contract with the contractor. Thus the employer may be regarded as being at the apex of a triangle by means of which the extent of the authority of a particular person is known to all parties concerned:

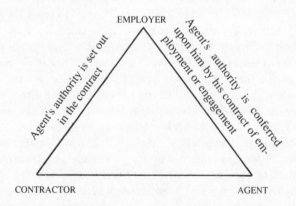

Where authority is conferred upon one person to act as agent of the other, this authority will often be expressed in an agreement, such as an appointment as engineer or project manager, and we may call this form of authority **actual authority**. It is the authority that that person has really been given. It may, in some instances, arise by *implication* out of an appointment, since a person who is given a particular job description may reasonably suppose that he has, by an implied agreement with the body appointing him, all the authority to do things that are usual for a person having that appointment to do. These arrangements are all made between the employer and his agent, and they alone are parties to these arrangements. The point of conveying to the contractor the name or names of the persons who are entitled to carry out certain functions concerning the project, such as issuing variations orders, is to make it clear to the contractor that he is only entitled to act upon the authority of the person or persons named, and no others. If he then acts upon the instructions of any other person, the employer will be able to repudiate the instructions, by stating that the person giving them had no authority to do so and that this fact was *known to the contractor*.

The knowledge of the contractor is important, because the employer may not deny things which are within the *apparent authority* of his agent. Apparent authority exists where the employer allows the contractor to think that a particular person is authorised to carry out a particular function when that person is not in fact authorised. It may, for example, occur in relation to a project, where a number of people are employees of the employer and are involved in the project, and where the precise chain of command has not been properly brought to the attention of the contractor. The *internal procedures* may be known to the employer and his employees, but they may not be known to the contractor. In such a case, the apparent authority of certain people may be greater then their actual authority. What this means for the employer is that the necessary emphasis must be placed upon bringing matters of authority to the attention of the contractor, *and* upon enforcing the internal procedures for dealing with matters relating to the project. Otherwise it is possible for an employer to find himself committed to a particular decision by an employee who oversteps the mark, but who, as far as the contractor is concerned, has apparent authority to take the decision. The employee is of course answerable to the employer for this, but this is not much help to the employer, who may find himself legally bound to pay for the decision.

PERFORMANCE OF THE CONTRACT UNDER THE DIRECTION AND SUPERVISION OF THE EMPLOYER'S AGENT OR NOMINEE

We may end this chapter with a look at a further issue of great importance in building and engineering contracts: many contracts call for work to be carried out and executed not only in accordance with a specification, but also to the approval or satisfaction of a person named in the contract, such as an architect or an engineer. Tests and inspections may have to satisfy certain stated criteria, or they may, again, have to meet the approval or satisfaction of the person named. As we have seen, an employee or architect or engineer or other agent is the agent of the employer, and not of the contractor. This raises the question of his objectivity or neutrality, and the extent to which his decisions can be

113

overridden, and the extent to which he may be liable to one or the other of the parties for his decisions.

There is no doubt that an agent may be liable to his principal, and as such an architect or engineer may certainly be liable for a failure to carry out his functions properly, whether those functions are in the area of design or approval of drawings, or approval of materials or other similar functions. Thus in New Zealand, both an architect and a consulting engineer were held to be liable for a faulty design of the structural part of a sports centre: *Bevan Investments Ltd* v *Blackhall and Struthers* (1973). In Canada, naval architects have been held to be liable for failure to make further inquiries about the suitability of materials to be used in a project: *Sealand of the Pacific* v *McHaffie Ltd* (1974). In England, the case of *Pirelli General Cable Works Ltd* v *Oscar Faber and Partners* (1982), shows that this principle holds good, although the liability in question was not established in that case because the action was time-barred. The details of this case will be looked at in the final chapter. It should be noted that liability in this area may arise either in contract, or in tort, for negligence, or, in some cases, both forms of liability may be established.

However, until the last few decades, there was some doubt about the position of the architect or engineer in his *certifying capacity*. For some time it had been thought that in this capacity his position was that of an arbitrator, and that therefore he could not be liable for negligence. The decision of the House of Lords in the case of *Sutcliffe* v *Thakrah* (1974) was that in certifying, an architect (and presumably an engineer as well) was *not an arbitrator, and could be liable for negligence*. In this instance the architects and quantity surveyors had been sued for negligence because defective work, and work which had not been done at all, had been certified, and payments had been made to the contractor. The contractor had subsequently been dismissed by the employer and had become insolvent. On the other hand, errors in certificates will not normally render an architect or engineer liable to the contractor. There is no contract between the architect or engineer and the *contractor*, and a case of negligence will be difficult to make out. This issue arose in the case of *Lubenham Fidelities and Investment Co Ltd* v *South Pembrokeshire District Council and Wigley Fox Partnership* (1986). In this case the plaintiff was the successor to a firm of contractors in a building contract. (This occurred because the original contractor had gone into liquidation, and the plaintiff, as bondsman, had elected to perform the contract.) The architect had mistakenly advised the employer, which was the local authority, to deduct liquidated damages from interim certificates. One of the questions which arose in this case was whether or not this entitled the plaintiff to cease work. It was held that it did not. The other question to arise was whether or not the architects were liable to the plaintiff for the mistaken decision. The court held that liability did not arise in this case. The court stated that for liability to occur an architect had to have the necessary intention to interfere with the rights of the contractor. An error in a certificate did not by itself amount to this, although it could arise if an architect or engineer were to misapply the provisions of a contract deliberately so as to deprive the contractor of money to which he was entitled.

The approval or satisfaction of the architect or engineer

Contracts differ widely on the nature of the contractor's obligations. In some contracts the contractor will simply be required to complete or deliver work or goods according to a specification. In others, he will have to do these things not only according to a specification, but also to the approval or satisfaction of another party. This other party may be the employer himself, or an employee or other appointee of the employer, or he may be an independent third party, such as a local authority, or other certifying authority. To give an example, the JCT (1980) form of building contract states that:

> 'The Contractor shall upon and subject to the Conditions carry out and complete the Works shown upon the Contract Drawings and described by or referred to in the Specification and in the Articles of Agreement, the Conditions and the Appendix ... in compliance therewith, using materials and workmanship of the quality and standards therein specified, provided that where and to the extent that approval of the quality of materials or of the standards of workmanship is a matter for the opinion of the Architect, such quality and standards shall be to the reasonable satisfaction of the Architect.'

Under this clause, work and materials must, to a certain extent, meet the reasonable satisfaction of the architect. The test of 'reasonable satisfaction' will be an objective one, and when certifying, the architect will be under an obligation to act independently of the employer or contractor.

Not all contracts are the same, and the differences between them in this particular area may present problems of interpretation of excruciating difficulty. For example, the word 'reasonable' does not necessarily appear in all forms of contract (and in some forms of foreign contracts it has been noticeably absent). If the approval or satisfaction which is required is that of the *employer*, English courts will, as a matter of construction, probably *imply* that the withholding of such approval or satisfaction must be reasonable and not capricious, and additionally, the courts will require that a refusal to approve work must be genuine and honest: bad faith on the part of an employer will not entitle him to withhold payment. However, the criterion of reasonableness will not be easy to imply where matters of taste or aesthetics are concerned, and here the employer will be entitled to withhold approval as long as he does so in good faith.

If the approval or satisfaction mentioned in the contract is that of a third party, including an architect or engineer in his certifying capacity, it is less likely that the courts will imply that his opinion must be reasonable. This is because the opinion will be one that is given independently of both the contractor and the employer. The JCT form of contract, Clause 2 of which was, in part, quoted earlier, *adds* the requirement of reasonableness, as do many other forms of contract. Contractors require this, and a comprehensive arbitration clause, for their protection, wherever matters of opinion or satisfaction arise in a contract. Without provisions protecting the contractor, it is not easy for him to contest the opinion of an architect or engineer in his certifying capacity. In the case of *Minster Trust Ltd* v *Traps Tractors Ltd* (1954) Mr Justice DEVLIN stated:

'What has to be ascertained in each case is whether the agent is or is not intended to function independently of the principal ... The main test appears to be whether the certificate is intended to embody a decision that is final and binding on the parties. If it is, then it is in effect an award, and it has the attributes of its arbitral character. It cannot be attacked on the ground that it is unreasonable, as the opinion of a party or the certificate of one who is merely an agent probably can.'

The new MF/1 form of Engineering Contract

This new 1988 form of contract contains a specific clause defining the Engineer's duties. The Engineer is to carry out the duties specified in the contract; the contractor is to carry out the work in accordance with the engineer's decisions, instructions and orders; the Engineer is, by a sub-clause of the clause in question, specifically required to exercise his discretion *fairly*. This emphasises the point made in the previous paragraph, and, in this respect, the Engineer under this form of contract is not a mere agent or servant of his principal.

The effect of certificates

Many forms of contract provide that the employer or his architect or engineer shall *certify* that certain events have taken place, such as delivery or completion of work, or performance of the equipment in certain tests, or taking over of the equipment. The object of provisions about certificates in a contract is to provide for proper documentation against which payment is made: the certificates not only record that payment is due, but also record the amount of payment which is due.

If contracts provide for certificates, then they should provide details about how application for certificates is to be made; who is to make such application, and to whom; when such application is to be made, and when the certificates are to be issued; what is to be included in a certificate; how certificates are to be adjusted or corrected; the grounds upon which certificates may or may not be withheld; the relationship of the certificates to payment; and the legal effect of certificates.

As far as the legal effect of certificates is concerned, different contracts state different things, so that one must always study these provisions of a contract with care. Some contracts say nothing about the legal effect of any of the certificates provided for, other than that payment is due within a certain number of days of the amount certified. Other contracts go further and provide *specific remedies* for the contractor in the event of a failure by the employer to make payment when due. Even if specific remedies are not mentioned as such, it is of course a breach of contract by an employer to fail to pay the amount certified. This is to be distinguished from an error in a certificate, which if made by an architect or engineer, is not a breach of contract by the employer: see *Lubenham Fidelities and Investment Co Ltd* v *South Pembrokeshire District Council* (1986), cited in chapter 2 of this work. Errors in certificates should, if in interim certificates, be corrected at the next stage; errors in final certificates should be corrected by arbitration (a good reason why engineering and building contracts should contain arbitration clauses).

There is another important legal effect which a certificate may have: a certificate is a statement made by an employer or his architect or engineer. It can therefore be used as *evidence*, if a dispute should arise. The question is then to what *extent* it can be relied upon as evidence. Some contracts say nothing about this, in which case the status of a certificate as evidence of a matter to which it relates will depend upon what it states in the certificate, as well as on its context. On the other hand, some forms of contract, such as the JCT, or the Model form A, or MF/1, contain clauses which *define the status of certificates as evidence*. It is normal, in this respect, to make a distinction between an *interim certificate* and a *final certificate*. Interim certificates will normally be stated *not* to be conclusive evidence of any matter stated in them. The reason for this will be so that an interim certificate will not prejudice the rights of either of the parties against the other. As to the final certificate, which is the certificate which certifies the total amount payable to the contractor under the contract, and which is normally only issued when the work is completed and the defects liability period has expired and remedial work, if any, has been done, the effect of this as evidence will depend *precisely* upon what the contract says. If a clause in the contract says that the final certificate is to be *conclusive evidence* of a matter, then, *as far as that matter is concerned, the final certificate really is final*, and the matter cannot be raised again between the parties (except perhaps by mutual consent as a matter of goodwill).

However, most contracts which contain conclusive evidence clauses make exceptions for fraud, and for matters referred to arbitration within a certain period. Moreover, the finality will only attach to those matters specifically mentioned in the conclusive evidence clause, so that other issues will not necessarily be final. Having said this, employers should scrutinise such clauses carefully before agreeing to them, since such clauses do give their architects or engineers power to some extent to sign away some of their rights, and it is important that the clause should be written so as to be fair and reasonable.

8 Sub-contracting

Sub-contracting is of great importance in building and engineering contracts, and presents many legal issues. It is comparatively rare for a project of any magnitude to be carried out by a single contractor, and inevitably work will be sub-contracted to specialists. In this chapter we must analyse the relationships that are created, as between the employer, his contractor, and the sub-contractors; we must also examine issues about property rights, and liability for the quality or performance of sub-contracted goods or work.

Agency and sub-contracting compared

It is helpful to make the distinction between cases where a customer buys goods through an **agent** and cases where a customer buys goods from a contractor who has himself bought the goods from a sub-contractor. One must bear in mind at all times that the description of the parties is not necessarily accurate or conclusive, and the precise nature of the legal relationship can only be discovered by careful analysis of the facts.

In an agency relationship, a person dealing with a buyer's agent is, in effect, dealing with the buyer himself. Thus he has a direct contractual relationship with the buyer, and direct recourse to the buyer for payment. And it follows that the buyer who deals with a seller through an agent has a direct claim against the seller in respect of the goods or services concerned.

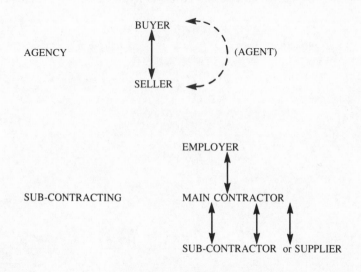

When work is sub-contracted, the standard meaning of the expression is that the main contractor makes a contract with the employer, and makes one or more separate contracts with sub-contractors or suppliers. There will therefore be two or more separate contracts. Except in special cases, the parties will have recourse only against those with whom they have contracts. This has an important effect upon matters such as payment, ownership of goods and materials, and issues relating to the quality of goods or services. Two cases may serve to illustrate the legal differences between agency and sub-contracting.

In *Teheran-Europe and Co Ltd* v *S T Belton (Tractors) Ltd* (1968), the buyer, T, was a foreign concern. Its *agent*, a company called R Ltd, negotiated a purchase of air-compressor units from S T Belton (Tractors) Ltd, an English company. After the goods had been delivered to Iran, a claim arose regarding the suitability of the goods for use in that country. The issue before the Court of Appeal was whether or not T was entitled to enforce its claim in respect of the fitness of the goods for their purpose against S T Belton Ltd. T could only do this if it could he established that R Ltd had acted as *agent* for T, and had thus set up a contract between T and S T Belton Ltd. The Court of Appeal examined the correspondence between R Ltd and S T Belton, part of which read as follows:

> 'Dear Sirs
> Dorman air pumps/mobile compressors. We have been in communication with our clients and have been instructed to put forward an offer to purchase 12 units at £300 each delivered London packers exclusive of any form of packing and to proceed immediately with shipment of the first two units. We shall be obliged to have your acceptance to this giving us the approximate date for the earliest delivery.'

The Court of Appeal did not find this entirely free from ambiguity, but it held that there was in fact a relationship of agency in this case, and that as principal, T was entitled to maintain its claim directly against the seller, S T Belton. (In fact the claim failed, on the ground that T had not established that it had relied upon the skill and judgment of the seller in the matter of suitability for use in Iran.)

Coincidentally, the next case also concerns goods which were destined for Iran, and it illustrates the fact that if the relationship between the parties involves *sub-contracting*, each contractual relationship must be considered as a separate issue.

In *Redler Grain Silos* v *BICC Ltd* (1982), a contract was made between RGS and an Iranian government organisation for the building of works in Iran. In 1980, RGS ordered electrical cable and other equipment from BICC Ltd, to be delivered from the UK to Khorramshahr, C & F, in October 1980. The Iranian government body had made advance payments to RGS, and in June 1980 RGS paid BICC Ltd the full price of the goods in return for a performance bond.

By October 1980, troubles in Iran had made shipment risky and perhaps impossible. It was then agreed that the parties to the sub-contract should vary their contract, and that RGS should take delivery from BICC Ltd in the UK. The Iranian Government body then laid claim to the cable and other

119

equipment, claiming to be the owner, by virtue of having paid RGS in advance. This claim was opposed by RGS, which argued that the contract for sale of goods by BICC Ltd was made with RGS, and was capable of conferring rights on RGS alone. The court held that this was indeed the case, and that the property in the goods had in fact passed to RGS, and that the goods could not be handed over to another party.

Notes

(a)   It was important to RGS, the main contractor, to retain the goods, so that it alone had the right to do the required work for its customer.

(b)   The Iranian government organisation was the employer. Its contract was with RGS. The sub-contract between RGS and BICC was a separate contract to which they alone were parties. Thus only RGS could acquire title to goods under this sub-contract. The title of the Iranian organisation would then depend upon its own contract with RGS.

(c)   This case also illustrates the point already made in an earlier chapter, that advance payment in respect of goods does not of itself confer title upon the buyer. Title passes according to the terms of each contract.

FORMING SUB-CONTRACTS

In general there is an implied right, in the absence of contrary provisions in the main contract, to delegate or sub-contract for goods and materials or parts of the work of a contract. This is subject to the duty of the main contractor to continue to maintain control and responsibility and to observe his general obligations with regard to the project. Thus there is *no* implied right to delegate in such a way as to alter or prejudice the rights of the employer to have the work done under the control of the contractor he selects, or to delegate in such a way as to alter the legal position of the employer. In practice, many contracts contain specific provisions about sub-contracting. Some conditions, usually written by sellers and contractors, will state that the seller or contractor has the right to appoint agents and sub-contractors to perform any part of his obligations. Other forms of contract, either written by employers, or of a 'national' nature, may contain provisions restricting or prohibiting sub-contracting. For example, the JCT (1980) form of building contract states:

'19.1   Neither the employer nor the Contractor shall, without the written consent of the other, assign this contract.

19.2   The Contractor shall not without the written consent of the Architect (which consent shall not be unreasonably withheld) sub-let any portion of the works . . .'

To assign is to hand over the entire contract, and it is common for the parties expressly to prohibit this. In fact the common law would in any case prohibit the assignment by either party of his *liabilities*, such as the duty to perform the work, or the duty to pay. However, unless the contract states the contrary, the law does allow the assignment of *rights*, such as the right to receive payment.

This is done under many 'factoring' agreements. The validity of a clause prohibiting the assignment of rights has been thought open to doubt, but in *Helstan Securities* v *Hertfordshire C C* (1978), such a clause was held to be effective, where it stated that the contractor was prohibited from assigning the contract or any benefit or interest therein. The court held that an assignment by the contractor of money due, without consent, was invalid because of this provision.

Provisions in contracts prohibiting *sub-contracting*, or requiring permission to be given by the employer, will be enforceable. That is why it is advisable, from the point of view of the contractor, to have the provisions drafted in such a way that the necessary permission 'shall not be unreasonably withheld'. Without these words, permission to sub-contract is entirely a matter for the employer.

Assuming that the contract is one in which the main contractor is permitted to sub-contract work, a straightforward situation will be one in which the main contractor, having formed the contract which constitutes the main contract, will then enter into the necessary sub-contracts with the sub-contractors. The main contractor will, in this situation, have the advantage of knowing the precise obligations which are placed upon him by the main contract, and will endeavour to form sub-contracts which are consistent with and which will facilitate the main contract, and which will offer the main contractor the protection which he will require. Ideally, the main contractor will have *negotiated* the various sub-contracts before he becomes bound by the main contract, so that on signing the main contract, the tenders, quotations, or other offers to do sub-contracted work will be open for acceptance on terms which are known and agreed. Of course, the timing of these matters can vary a great deal, and perfection cannot always be achieved. But to make binding contracts for sub-contracted work before the main contract is agreed leaves the main contractor open to the risk that the main contract will be altered at the last moment, or fall through; while to sign the main contract without having negotiated the terms of the more important sub-contracts leaves the main contractor in a vulnerable position, since he may not find sub-contractors willing to give him delivery dates or guarantees which are consistent with the main contract obligations. Needless to say, it should never be assumed by main contractors that they will necessarily obtain 'back-to-back' conditions of contract (ie those under which sub-contractors will undertake similar obligations to those of the main contract). Such conditions must always be negotiated.

In modern engineering projects, the formation of contracts and sub-contracts can be much more complicated than the previous paragraph suggests. It is not necessarily the case that the employer will appoint his main contractor first. In many cases the reputation, or technical abilities, or competitive prices, of the sub-contractor, will be of greater importance to the employer than the work of the main contractor, and the employer will have negotiated directly with one or more sub-contractors long before a main contractor is appointed. The main contractor will then be expected to form contracts with the sub-contractors whose names are put forward by the employer. It will be important, in such cases, to know whether or not the sub-contractors in question are 'nominated' sub-contractors, or 'domestic' sub-contractors, and to what extent the main contractor is responsible for the delays or defective work of such sub-contractors.

'Domestic sub-contractors'

This expression is used in this work in the same sense as it is used in JCT forms of contract, that is, to mean those sub-contractors which are not 'nominated sub-contractors'.

'Nominated sub-contractors'

These are those sub-contractors which are named, selected or approved or otherwise chosen by an instruction of the employer or his architect or engineer or other representative. If the final selection is that of the employer, etc, there is little difficulty in identifying those sub-contractors which are 'nominated'. One difficulty which arises is the position where the contract provides for a *list* of persons from whom the main contractor is to select his sub-contractors. This might create some doubt as to the status of the sub-contractors selected by this method, and the safest thing to do in such circumstances is to ensure that the main contract defines clearly the status of such sub-contractors, as does the JCT (1980) form of building contract, which, broadly speaking, provides that such sub-contractors are classified as *domestic* sub-contractors, as long as the list comprises at least three persons, and as long as the main contractor has the sole discretion as to the final selection.

Position of sub-contractors

Each sub-contractor, whether nominated or domestic, is responsible to the main contractor with whom he has his contract. (We will call such a person *a main contractor* in this chapter, for the sake of simplicity, although in reality there may well be an extended chain of supply, in which work is first sub-contracted, then sub-sub-contracted, and so on.)

Negotiations with the employer do not by themselves bring the sub-contractor into a binding contract. Nor does the fact of nomination, approval, or selection have this effect. The only thing which can bring a sub-contractor into a binding contract is the formation of a contract, by the usual process of offer and acceptance, between the sub-contractor and the main contractor.

When main contractors contract with sub-contractors, they either make those contracts on specially prepared forms of sub-contract, which can be obtained from national organisations such as the JCT, or they may make the contracts on their own 'conditions of purchase', which should be drawn up in such a way as to be consistent with the main contractor's obligations under his contract with the employer, or they may make the sub-contracts by *reference* to certain terms and conditions. This last method is fraught with difficulties, particularly if more than one set of conditions is referred to, or if the conditions referred to do not appear to be designed for sub-contracts. In the case of *Brightside Kilpatrick*

Engineering Services v *Mitchell Construction Ltd* (1975), the Court of Appeal had to consider the position where B was nominated as a sub-contractor, and M placed the order on an order form which stated that the sub-contract documents would consist of a *standard form of tender*, a *specification, conditions of contract*, and a *schedule of facilities*. The order stated that the form of the contract with the employer was RIBA 1963, Revised July 1971. The order then stated that 'the conditions applicable to the sub-contract shall be those embodied in RIBA as above agreement'. Lord Justice BUCKLEY stated:

'It is not an easy point, for, as so often happens when parties try to import into their contractual relationships terms in other documents which do not easily fit those relationships, it is difficult to know what is the proper construction to put upon the documents in the case.'

One argument was that the contract contained *all* the RIBA 1963/1971 conditions, substituting for the employer, references to the contractor, and substituting for the contractor, references to the sub-contractor. This, however, was not the approach taken by the court, because many of the clauses were inappropriate for this kind of approach. The alternative approach was to take the reference as being *only* to those conditions of the head contract *which specifically dealt with matters relating to sub-contractors*. This was the approach that was in fact taken by the Court of Appeal. This case demonstrates that although the courts will do their best to give effect to the presumed intentions of the parties, the parties will not, unless they take a great deal of care in these matters, necessarily obtain the precise result that they had anticipated.

The sub-contractor and the employer

The sub-contractor may in many cases have an important and lasting *commercial* relationship with the employer. This does not necessarily mean that the sub-contractor has any legal relationship with the employer. Indeed, in most cases, the most fundamental relationships of the sub-contractor are not with the employer, but with the main contractor. These relationships are those concerning performance of the work under the contract, and payment.

The work which a sub-contractor performs is performed for the main contractor, to the specification and within the time limits imposed upon the sub-contractor by the sub-contract. If the sub-contractor is not legally bound to perform within a given time, and if the project is held up, the employer may take action, such as the levying of liquidated damages, against the main contractor, but this does not necessarily make the sub-contractor liable, or even ensure that the work is performed on time. This was precisely the position in the case of *British Steel Corporation* v *Cleveland Bridge and Engineering Co Ltd* (1981), in which the contractor *CBE* was unable to obtain delivery according to its exact requirements, and was unable to make its sub-contractor liable for this, since the sub-contractor had not agreed the required delivery dates or sequence.

The sub-contractor does not normally give to the employer any direct undertakings about quality. The sub-contractor's undertakings, which may be express or implied, are given to the main contractor. If there are direct

123

negotiations between the employer and the sub-contractor, it may be that the sub-contractor will give direct, express, guarantees to the employer. These will be in addition to those given by the contractor to the employer.

Payment of the sub-contractor is of course made by the party with whom he is in contract, ie the main contractor. The terms of payment will depend entirely upon the terms of the sub-contract, and there is no rule that they must necessarily relate to the terms of the main contract: the matter is one for negotiation between the parties to each contract at the time that it is made. Some contractors attempt to operate a 'pay when paid' system, under which they do not release the money to their sub-contractors until they have received the money from the employer. While this may perhaps be understandable from a financial point of view, it should be pointed out that this is in many cases completely inconsistent with the terms of payment in the sub-contracts, and that to operate it *de facto* will in such cases, almost certainly put the main contractor in breach of his contracts with the sub-contractors.

In general, there is *no* direct payment between the employer and the sub-contractor. This simple proposition is the corollary of the law of privity of contract, which lays down the principle that only the parties to a contract can enforce it. However, this simple rule may be complicated by a number of factors.

(a)   The 'sub-contractor' may only be a sub-contractor in name, but may in fact be directly under contract to the employer. This is sometimes the case, particularly where the employer buys specialised equipment or goods for a contract, and decides to buy them directly from the supplier, and not through the main contractor. In such cases, the goods will be paid for by the employer, and the supplier of the goods will give direct undertakings to the employer.

(b)   The main contract may contain provisions for direct payment of sub-contractors by the employer. These exist in JCT forms of building contract, in relation to nominated sub-contractors, in certain circumstances.

(c)   The main contract and the sub-contracts may operate in such a way that *retention money* held by the employer is held in trust, and a proportion of it is held in trust for the sub-contractors. This was held to be the case in *Re Arthur Sanders Ltd* (1981), under the RIBA 1963 forms of contract when used with the 1963 FAS form of contract. In this case the Greater London Council was held to be liable to pay some of the retention money to the liquidator of the main contractor (which was being wound up) to be passed on to the nominated sub-contractors.

TITLE TO GOODS IN PROJECTS INVOLVING SUB-CONTRACTED WORK

The *main* contract will regulate matters of title as between the main contractor and the employer. Nothing in the main contract can affect the title of the *sub-*

contractor, as such. The position of the sub-contractor will depend upon his contract with and his dealings with the main contractor. However, the main contract can, and often does, dictate to the main contractor the terms on which he is to form his contracts with his sub-contractors. This will therefore mean that the main contract has the effect of indirectly controlling the rights that exist or come into being under the sub-contracts. However, it is important that employers who wish to exert this form of control over sub-contracts should take steps to ensure that the sub-contracts are in fact made in the desired form. A failure to do this will mean that there is no certainty that a sub-contractor may not have contracted on his own terms, under which he may have retained title to goods after delivery either to site or to the main contractor. This we saw in the case of *Dawber Williamson Roofing Ltd* v *Humberside County Council* (1979), which was discussed in chapter 4.

However, if the terms of the *sub-contract* are correctly written (from the point of view of the employer), then the sub-contractor who has delivered goods to site will not be able to set up his title against the employer so as to defeat the claims of an employer who has already paid his main contractor for the goods. The problem in the *Dawber Williamson* case, for the County Council, was that the Council had paid the main contractor for materials of the sub-contractor. The main contractor had not paid the sub-contractor, and the main contractor had become insolvent. The *main contract* stated that where the value of unfixed materials or goods had been included in an interim certificate under which the contractor had received payment, such materials and goods would become the property of the employer. However, there was *no similar provision* in the sub-contract. As a result, the main contractor did not acquire title to the goods, and had no title to pass to the employer.

In contrast, in the much earlier case of *Pritchett and Gold and Electrical Power Storage Co* v *Currie* (1916), the terms of the sub-contract, which was a sale of goods, rather than a contract for work and materials, were not such as to prevent the main contractor from acquiring title on delivery. There was a direct delivery to site:

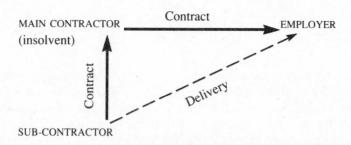

The court held here, that the sub-contractor had passed title to the main contractor, under the normal rules of passing of property in a sale of goods. The sub-contractor was therefore not entitled to the return of the goods. Nor did the sub-contractor have any direct claim against the employer for money, since the employer's duty to pay was owed to the main contractor.

It will be noted here that the difference between the two cases cited in the previous paragraphs is one of construction of the terms of the sub-contract. In the *Dawber Williamson* case, the sub-contract was for *work and materials*. It followed that, unless there was an express provision to the contrary, title would remain with the sub-contractor until the goods were fixed. In the *Pritchett and Gold* case, the contract was one of *sale of goods*. Under the law of sale of goods, title passes, in many cases, when goods are unconditionally appropriated to the contract, and therefore was lost to the sub-contractor upon delivery to site. From these fine distinctions, it will be apparent that clear, well written clauses concerning the passing of property in goods and materials are an essential part of contracting and sub-contracting.

QUALITY AND FITNESS

In the normal course of events, each party to a contract gives express and implied undertakings about the quality and fitness of goods and workmanship to the party with whom he is in contract and who is purchasing goods and services from him. Thus the main contractor will give undertakings to the employer, and the sub-contractors will give undertakings to the main contractor, and sub-sub-contractors will give undertakings to those sub-contractors with whom they have contracts, and so on. Thus, if a defective item is found in the work which is done for the employer, liability for its defective quality, or failure to conform with description, or unfitness for the purpose for which it is required will be placed upon each contracting party which is responsible for the supply of that item, in succession, until the liability eventually comes to rest upon the party which is responsible for the existence of the defect.

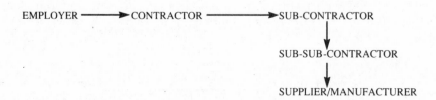

Some important points must be made about the principle of the 'chain of liability' which is illustrated above. Firstly, in most cases, the main contractor is primarily liable to the employer. He cannot simply 'pass on' responsibility to the sub-contractor or other parties: it is the main contractor's liability, although once the main contractor has accepted that liability, he may then look to *his* contract with his sub-contractor to have any loss which he sustains made good. Secondly, because the responsibility is that of the main contractor, he must beware of factors which could weaken his recourse to his sub-contractors, or in some cases deprive him of recourse altogether. Such factors include the possibility that the sub-contractor in question may be insolvent or a 'man of straw'. It is also possible that unequal undertakings may have been given, so that the contractor warrants his materials, but a particular sub-contractor has not given undertakings in similar terms, because of the circumstances under which the sub-contracted goods were specified. We have seen an example of this in the case of *Aswan Engineering Establishment Co* v *Lupdine Ltd (Thurgar Bolle Ltd*, third party) (1986), which is set out in chapter 5.

Other dangers for a contractor include the possibility that a sub-contractor may have limited or excluded liability by means of a valid exclusion or limitation of liability clause, while the contractor may have no such exclusion or limits in his contract with his employer. Another possibility is that the statutory time limits for legal action may have expired in one contract but not in another, because of work being completed at different times under different contracts. We will have more to say about this in the final chapter of this work, but it is worth noting that this was in fact the case in *Young and Marten Ltd* v *McManus Childs Ltd* (1969). In this case, a developer of property employed a roofing contractor to fix tiles to houses on an estate. The contractor obtained the tiles through a sub-contractor, who also fixed the tiles. The tiles proved to be defective. It was held by the House of Lords that the roofing contractor was liable to the developer, under the implied term that goods should be of merchantable quality. However, the roofing contractor was unable in this case to join the sub-contractor into the proceedings, since the statutory time limits for bringing legal proceedings had expired against the sub-contractor.

Does it make any difference whether or not the sub-contractor is nominated?

In general it makes no difference at all, whether the sub-contractor is classed as a nominated sub-contractor, or as a domestic sub-contractor, as far as liability of the main contractor for defective goods or work and materials is concerned. This is shown by the case of *Young and Marten Ltd* v *McManus Childs Ltd* (1969), where the tiles in question came from only one manufacturer, so that the contractor had to buy from that manufacturer, or from somebody who bought from him. Lord REID stated:

> 'Why should that make any difference? It would make a difference if that manufacturer was only willing to sell on terms which excluded or limited his ordinary liability under the Sale of Goods Act and that fact was known to the employer and the contractor when they made their contract.'

The case of *Independent Broadcasting Authority and EMI* v *BICC* (1980), which was discussed in chapter 5, also illustrates this point: EMI had responsibility for the matters in respect of which it had given an undertaking to its employer – in this case, design and suitability – notwithstanding that the design and workmanship was in fact that of a nominated sub-contractor. The House of Lords found in this case that there was nothing unreasonable in reaching this conclusion, since EMI had the right to check the design, and had contracted for the design, and had the right to recover, in turn, from BICC who did the actual designing.

In general, it can be said, as a result of the two cases cited above, that where a sub-contractor is nominated, the main contractor nearly always takes responsibility for goods which are not merchantable. Whereas 'design responsibility' is a rather more complex issue, and depends upon the contract between the employer and the main contractor. In *Young and Marten Ltd* v *McManus Childs Ltd*, the goods were found to be unmerchantable. Had they merely been the wrong type of goods for the particular purpose, the roofing contractor would not have been liable to the developer, because the developer alone had been responsible for the choice of that particular type of tile.

Exceptionally, as stated by Lord REID in the quotation given above, there can be cases where *no* implied terms as to quality are given by the main contractor to the employer. This situation is most likely to arise in the context of a *nominated sub-contractor* or a *nominated supplier*, as was demonstrated by the case of *Gloucestershire County Council* v *Richardson* (1969). In this case, the form of contract used by the employer (the Council) was the RIBA 1939 contract, 1957 revision. It included a prime cost sum for the supply of pre-cast pre-stressed concrete columns. The contract gave to the main contractor the right to make reasonable objections to the nomination of *sub-contractors*. No equivalent right of objection was given regarding the nomination of *suppliers*. Suppliers of the concrete columns had been nominated. The suppliers sold on their own terms of sale, which excluded liability in respect of the columns, other than free replacement. The columns were delivered, and cracks appeared in them in the course of erection. Work was held up, and the main contractor eventually determined the contract with the Council. The validity of this determination of the contract depended entirely upon the issue of whether or not the *main contractor* was in breach of *his* contract, as regards the quality of the columns. If the contractor was in breach, his determination of the contract was not good. If he was not in breach, then responsibility for the cessation of work did not lie with the contractor. The House of Lords held that the main contractor *had not given any implied warranty in respect of the quality of the columns*. They held that this situation differed greatly from that in *Young and Marten Ltd* v *McManus Childs Ltd*: as Lord PEARCE stated, to find the intention of the parties one must consider the express terms of the contract and any admissible surrounding circumstances. Here, the House of Lords thought that it was clear that a main contractor accepted liability for defective work done by a nominated *sub-contractor*, but the distinction between a sub-contractor and a *supplier*, in this particular form of contract, without a right of objection in the case of nominated suppliers, and in circumstances in which the particular supplier had excluded much of his liability to the main contractor, meant that it was difficult to *imply* that the main contractor had accepted liability in respect of the quality of the goods.

There are dangers in this position for employers, since, if they do not have a remedy against the contractor, they may be left without a remedy at all. In some cases they will demand and receive direct warranties from the nominated suppliers. In other cases they may be able to bring claims against nominated sub-contractors or suppliers for *negligence* (as happened in *IBA* v *EMI and BICC*). But direct warranties have to be specially negotiated, and negligence requires a heavy burden of proof. In the case of *Gloucestershire County Council* v *Richardson*, the employer had no remedy at all. Although cases such as this are the exception rather than the rule, employers should be careful not to do anything which might negative the conditions and warranties as to fitness and quality which are normally implied as between them and their main contractors.

DELAYS BY SUB-CONTRACTORS

In general a main contractor is either liable for delays under his contract with his employer, or he is not; depending upon the terms of the contract and the undertakings as to time (see chapter 3). If the main contractor is liable, delays by sub-contractors (of whatever description) are normally no excuse for such delays, and do not release or absolve the contractor from such liability. In some forms of contract, there are special clauses which *do* entitle the main contractor to an extension of time on the ground of delay by nominated sub-contractors. These clauses, which exist in RIBA forms of contract (up till 1980) and in the JCT (1980), are presumably inserted because the employer will have had the benefit of negotiations with the nominated sub-contractor, and will have had the opportunity to assess and take into account the track record of the nominated sub-contractor as far as completion on time is concerned. They can therefore be justified on commercial grounds. They have not, however, been universally admired, and there are those who would argue that such clauses deprive the employer of a great deal of protection as far as completion dates are concerned. For this reason, no doubt, the courts have construed such clauses narrowly, allowing an extension of time for 'delays', but *not* for 'defective work' by nominated sub-contractors. This was the decision in *Westminster Corporation* v *Jarvis* (1970), in which piling work was done by nominated sub-contractors; and the work proved to be partially defective. Westminster, the employer, claimed liquidated damages from the main contractor. Both the main contractor and the nominated sub-contractor disputed this, on the ground that the RIBA contract allowed for an extension of time for 'delay on the part of nominated sub-contractors . . . which the contractor has taken all practicable steps to avoid or reduce'. The argument of the main contractor and the sub-contractor was that the time taken to remedy the defects was such a delay, and that liquidated damages should not be charged in this respect. The House of Lords held that what had occurred was not a 'delay', since the sub-contractor had purportedly completed the work, and had left the site, before it became apparent that the piles were defective. This was held by the House of Lords to be defective work, but not to fall within the particular clause allowing an extension of time. It should be noted that in this case, as in many others, the main contractor was entitled to recover from the sub-contractor any losses caused by claims for liquidated damages by the employer, and consequently the party most concerned to argue in favour of an extension of time was the sub-contractor. One can only repeat that clauses allowing extensions of time for delays by sub-contractors are only found in a few forms of contract, and even then will be given a narrow interpretation.

9 Progress in Building and Engineering Projects

We have already encountered issues relating to time, in two previous chapters, concerning payment and delivery. In this chapter we will be looking at 'progress' from the point of view of contracts which are spread over considerable periods of time, as is the case with many building contracts, mechanical and electrical engineering contracts, chemical engineering contracts, as well as contracts for the petroleum industries, nuclear industry, steel industry, and shipbuilding and aerospace industries, to give a few examples. Here we will be considering how the contract can be used to facilitate progress in projects and to ensure that long-term programmes are met. We will also consider ways in which a contract can be used to cope with contingencies which may arise over a period of time, such as industrial disputes, natural disasters, legislation, hostilities, default by sub-contractors, changes, extras and variations – not all of these contingencies have the same legal effect, and we will be looking here at their effect on the obligations and financial position of the parties.

GETTING THE PROJECT COMPLETED ON TIME

In the law relating to contracts for work and materials, it is implied that work done under such contracts will be done within a reasonable time. This, however, is far too imprecise for modern requirements, and the best way in which to arrange for all matters relating to time for performance of obligations under a contract is to have clear provisions. Thus a good contract will probably state:

(a)   the time or programme for giving the contractor possession or admission to the site or to facilities for doing the work;

(b)   the requirement that the contractor submit a programme for carrying out and completing the work, and the time or date for submission of that programme;

(c)   completion date for the contract work;

(d)   dates for tests;

(e)   dates for the provision by the contractor of drawings, lists, data, manuals and other information.

This is not necessarily an exhaustive list. However, it will provide a convenient framework for the progress of the contract. It will need to be backed up by provisions in the *conditions* of the contract which provide for some or all of the following matters:

130

(i) Monitoring or review of the programme, and a right of the employer or his engineer to direct that the programme be altered, and the grounds (if any) on which this may be done. This is not only a useful adjunct to the right to vary the works, but it may, if properly written into the contract, be used to create and enforce 'recovery programmes', when work falls, for various reasons, behind the original programme.

(ii) Financial redress for the employer in the event of delay in the completion of the contract work. This is commonly achieved by means of liquidated damages provisions in the contract. If there are no provisions for liquidated damages, or if for some reason they cannot be enforced (as where they are held to be 'penalties', or where the completion date has not been inserted into the contract, or where the completion date has been invalidated), then the employer may still claim damages in respect of delay, *provided* that he can *prove loss* due to a breach of contract. This means that he must prove that dates or times or periods for carrying out work or furnishing goods or materials were given under the contract, *and* that they were not met, *and* that the employer has thereby suffered loss to the extent claimed. Whereas in order to claim liquidated damages, it is not necessary for the employer to prove that the actual loss suffered is the equivalent of the liquidated damages claimed.

(iii) Determination of the contract in the event of serious delay or default or failure to furnish a programme, or failure to make due and diligent progress according to the programme. This is really a 'long stop' provision in a contract, since in most cases the last thing an employer will wish to do is to dismiss a contractor, with all the ensuing difficulties of replacing that contractor and making claims for resulting loss. However, we have seen, earlier in this work, cases where employers have found it necessary to invoke such clauses to dismiss contractors who have delayed or suspended the work without good legal grounds.

Provisions of the kind described above are generally drafted for the benefit of employers or purchasers, since it is they who are primarily interested in undertakings as to time. However, a contract is a two-way undertaking, and both parties have an interest in matters relating to progress. The programme may in many respects protect the contractor as well as the employer, since matters such as the making available of the site or facilities may be made binding upon the employer, so that he is in breach of *his* obligations if he fails in this respect. Where site work is concerned, it is in fact an implied term of the contract that the employer will give the contractor possession of the site in sufficient time to enable him to fulfil his obligations within the time stated; but a clear programme with definite times or dates can only enhance this right of the contractor.

Liquidated damages provisions are initially written into contracts for the benefit of the customer or employer, but again, with suitable wording, a contractor can derive benefit from such provisions: indeed, one of the criticisms of liquidated damages, from the point of view of the employer, is that in many cases they do not provide sufficient incentive to the contractor to complete on time, since the contractor may have limited his liability to a small percentage, and may have allowed for this in his pricing of the contract. Some employers rely upon *bonuses*, as well as liquidated damages, to ensure that work is completed on time.

However, it would be unfair to suggest that it is *only* because of either the threat of damages, or the incentive of bonuses, that projects are completed on schedule. This is not by any means the case. There are many contracts where the legal remedies available to the employer exist, but do not have to be used, for the simple reason that the contractor is proud of his reputation for completion on or ahead of schedule, and will use all means to make sure that this is maintained. This work is about the law *and* the practice of building and engineering and commercial contracts, and although it is strongly recommended that employers and purchasers do their best to make sure that they have legal protection against delays under their contracts, it should not be forgotten that the ideal contract is one where they do not in practice have to be used, and where both parties have an agreed and workable programme and are working towards common goals.

THE EFFECT OF DELAYS

Occasionally in a project there will be, even with the best will on both sides, some event or obstruction which holds up progress and causes a delay and perhaps financial expense as well. The financial loss may be that of either party: the employer may lose revenue or the use of the item contracted for, while in some cases the contractor may be put to extra expense or may have to spend longer periods of time than he had budgeted for on a project, on account of a delay which may be the fault of another party. Questions that then arise are whether or not either party

(a)   has the right to alter the programme;

(b)   has the right to extend the overall time for completion of the work, and to set a new completion date;

(c)   is entitled to make a financial claim (including claims for liquidated damages, and claims for extra payment) against the other.

In each case one must make a careful record of the event which has caused the delay or departure from the programme and any resulting expense; the causes of this event must be identified. We may then classify the circumstances as falling within one of the following categories:

(i)   an act or omission or default on the part of the **contractor** resulting in his failure to meet the contract dates or the programme;

(ii)   an act or omission or default by the **employer** which obstructs the performance by the contractor of his duties or which necessitates additional time for the contractor to complete the work;

(iii)   obstruction or hindrance of the work, or default by third parties or by sub-contractors or suppliers;

132

(iv)   circumstances beyond the control of either party.

(Where an architect or engineer is used, an act or omission or default or instruction by the architect or engineer will form an additional category similar to acts, etc, of the employer.)

Having identified the nature of the event, and recorded or estimated its effect on the programme, one must then look to the form of contract which is being used, to see what provisions it makes for dealing with matters of the type identified, for example, by way of liability of the contractor in some cases, or by way of extra payment and extra time, in other cases. The **procedures** and **time limits** for claims are often stated in contracts and are most important. The observations which follow are *general rules*, which must always be read *subject to any special exceptions or provisions* which are made in the particular contract.

(i)   *Progress held up by the contractor*
This is for the contractor to remedy at the contractor's own expense. If it results in a failure by the contractor to meet the overall completion date, (liquidated) damages may be payable by the contractor. If there is a failure to meet the programme or to make due and diligent progress, the contractor may be, in some forms of contract, required to accept changes to working methods or schedules in order to meet the programme or an adjusted programme. In some cases he runs the risk of being dismissed or replaced for the whole or part of the contract work.

(ii)   *Progress held up by the employer, or his architect or engineer*
Here the employer may have to pay additional sums to the contractor, either for expenses of a kind defined in the contract, or by way of damages for breach of contract. Not all contracts make specific provision for extra payment to the contractor, but some, such as the JCT, do, under the heading of 'Loss and expense caused by matters materially affecting regular progress of the Works'.

If nothing is provided in the contract, damages may be payable at common law, if the employer has caused loss to the contractor by failing to comply with his duties under the contract.

Furthermore, the *completion date* will be invalidated by a breach by the employer which disrupts progress. The employer will then need the power to set a new completion date, or he will be unable to enforce the time for completion of the contract work.

(iii)   *Progress held up by third parties*
This is a complicated issue, since a great deal will depend upon who the third parties are. If they are simply domestic sub-contractors to the main contractor, then any default or delay will be the liability of the main contractor to the employer, and it will be for the main contractor to try to recoup the loss against the offending sub-contractor.

If the third parties are employed directly by the employer and not by the main contractor, then any disruption will be equivalent to disruption by the employer.

133

If the delay or default is that of a *nominated sub-contractor*, the problem becomes more complex, and one must look at the precise details of the contract: see *Gloucestershire CC* v *Richardson*, already cited in the previous chapter, and *Westminster City Council* v *Jarvis* (1970). See also *Percy Bilton* v *Greater London Council* (1982), and *Bickerton and Sons Ltd* v *North West Metropolitan Regional Hospital Board* (1969), both of which cases are explained below.

(iv)   *Progress held up by circumstances beyond the control of the parties*
Most contracts provide for an extension of time due to circumstances which are beyond the control of either party. Sometimes these circumstances are defined in the contract, and sometimes not. Where they are not defined, there are likely to be debatable frontiers.

Most contracts do not provide for extra payment to the contractor on account of such circumstances.

If no provision is made in the contract, then the common law applies: see the paragraph on *force majeure and frustration* below.

FORCE MAJEURE AND FRUSTRATION

The law assumes that the parties to a contract will foresee all events, so far as possible, and take account of them in arranging matters of price and time, and other relevant matters. If a contractor wishes to give a fixed and firm price, and a definite time for delivery and completion, then he is entitled to do so, and the customer is entitled to accept it. It will be assumed that both parties have entered the transaction with their eyes open. The contractor will then be liable for late delivery, and will be unable to alter his prices, even if delivery is held up, or costs are increased, due to circumstances beyond his control, such as transportation problems. This places considerable risk on the contractor. The common law does not go very far towards assisting the contractor if circumstances beyond his control occur. We have *no* general common law principle of force majeure. What we do have is the rather more limited law of *frustration*.

Frustration means that if the subject matter, or performance, or completion of a contract has become illegal or impossible, or has changed so that it is something radically different from that originally contemplated, then the contract will be at an end. The obligation to complete work ceases, and expenses and sums at reasonable rates for work already done can be claimed by the contractor on a quantum meruit basis. Frustration operates on the basis that the parties are entitled in certain circumstances to claim that the performance of the contract is no longer what they promised to do. For example, the entire destruction of a site could make a building contract frustrated. The destruction of materials on site would not have this effect, since one or other of the parties would have undertaken to insure the materials and works. An outbreak of war would frustrate a contract to deliver goods to or perform work in the enemy country. On the other hand, hostilities between two countries, not involving the United Kingdom, would not necessarily frustrate the contract, since it may not be illegal under English law to continue trading with nationals of either country, and trade may not be physically impossible. The important thing about frustration is to recognise its limited nature. For example, in the case of *Davis Contractors* v *Fareham UDC* (1956), a contractor who had failed adequately to protect himself against shortages of labour and materials argued that his contract was frustrated by severe shortages of labour, which resulted in the contract taking almost three times the period of time contemplated to perform. It was held that the contractor had taken the risk, by not making adequate provision in the contract, and that the circumstances did not amount to frustration. The contractor was therefore bound to perform at the original price.

Because of the very narrow interpretation given to the meaning of frustration, under common law, the parties will normally wish to incorporate *express* terms dealing with circumstances beyond their control into the contract. This is perfectly permissible, and in building and engineering and other commercial contracts one usually sees a clause which refers either to force majeure, or to 'circumstances beyond the parties' control', or to 'relevant events', or to 'extension of time'. These clauses do not always refer to precisely the same events, and some refer to a list of events which is wider than circumstances beyond the control of either party, and include acts or omissions of the employer or the architect, and delays by nominated sub-contractors. Every clause must therefore be looked at most carefully to see which circumstances are contemplated. The expression *force majeure*, which was originally part of the Code Napoleon, has never received comprehensive definition in English law, although it is reasonably clear that it does not normally include defaults by the employer, or delays by sub-contractors. It does, however, include wars, natural disasters of the kind which cannot ordinarily be guarded against, strikes, and any other matters which the parties have expressly defined as being force majeure.

A clause in a contract dealing with force majeure and other relevant events will usually state that one or other of the parties may apply for an extension of time on these grounds. The clause may also state to whom application for an extension of time is to be made, the time limits within which such application is to be made, and the procedure by which it is to be made. Attention must be paid to these matters, since an incorrectly made application could deprive the seller or contractor of the extension of time to which he would otherwise be entitled, and leave him exposed to damages or liquidated damages for delay. In *Intertradex SA* v *Lesieur-Tourteaux SARL* (1978), a clause in the contract provided:

> 'Force majeure, strikes, etc: Sellers shall not be responsible for delay in shipment of the goods or any part thereof occasioned by any ... breakdown of machinery ... or any cause comprehended in the term *force majeure*. If delay in shipment is likely to occur for any of the above reasons, Shipper shall give notice to their buyers ... The notice shall state the reason(s) for the anticipated delay.'

Owing to a breakdown of the electrical distribution panel at the supplier's

135

factory, on 3 February 1973, and the fact that a replacement part had to be obtained from Germany, and owing to interruptions in the supply of raw materials for the factory, the suppliers were not able to deliver the full contract quantity of goods in April 1973 to the Sellers. This put the Sellers into a delay in shipment to their buyers. The buyers claimed damages for delay, and the Sellers argued that this delay was caused by 'breakdown of machinery', which was a relevant event in the above clause of the contract. However, the Sellers did not submit their claim of circumstances beyond their control in the right form, since there were in fact *two* causes of delay, the other being shortage of raw materials.

The Commercial Court held that:

(i)   there was *no case of frustration* here;
(ii)   there therefore had to be a valid claim for an extension of time *under the terms of the contract*;
(iii)   the notice given was bad, since it did not specify *both* causes of delay.

On appeal, the Court of Appeal agreed with this view, and sent the matter to the Board of Appeal of GAFTA (where the case had originally been arbitrated) to evaluate whether or not the breakdown of machinery would have been sufficient in itself to have justified the full period of delay. If it were not sufficient, then the Seller would be liable for damages.

As will be seen from this case, it is generally the seller or contractor who, if a delay occurs, will claim an extension of time, since this will relieve him of liability to pay damages or liquidated damages. However, the power to extend time can be of benefit to the employer as well.

Setting time at large: the release of liquidated damages

A contract can function without a precise completion date: there will then be a duty to complete within a reasonable time. Similarly, a contract can function without a provision for liquidated damages: the employer will, if he is able to prove a loss due to delay resulting from breach of contract by the contractor, be entitled to claim ordinary damages. However, neither of these two principles afford any great convenience to the employer who wishes to have completion by a precise date, and a swift and effective remedy, by way of liquidated damages, in the event of delay. Consequently, when an employer has set a definite completion date, and liquidated damages, he will wish to make sure that this is enforceable throughout the period of performance of the work. However, the prudent employer will be aware that it may be his *own* (or his architect's or engineer's) act or omission which is the cause of a delay. Such an act will, in some cases, mean that the contractor will not be able to complete on time. This will then 'release' the completion date, since the employer cannot enforce a completion date which he has himself made it impossible to adhere to. Time will be 'at large', in the sense that there will be no fixed, contractually binding time for completion of the work. Without a completion date, liquidated damages cannot be recovered: the employer is then left to his *common law* remedies, of claiming such damages as he can prove to have resulted from any delay which is the fault of the contractor.

However, if the contract provides for an extension of time on account of delay caused by some act or omission or breach or default of the employer or his representatives, then the position is different. The parties will be taken to have intended that the employer will be able to enforce a completion date and, where appropriate, to recover liquidated damages, notwithstanding that the employer may himself have been at least partly the cause of some of the delay. Thus in the case of *Percy Bilton Ltd* v *Greater London Council* (1982), where there was a delay caused by the withdrawal of a nominated sub-contractor, and the length of the delay was partly attributable to the employer delaying in nominating a replacement sub-contractor, the House of Lords held that an extension of time could be given to cover the employer's part of the delay, while the contractor was to suffer the deduction of liquidated damages for the part of the delay which was not the fault of the employer. This case raised two interesting points: firstly, the employer has, in many cases involving nominated sub-contractors, the duty to *re-nominate*, that is, to find another sub-contractor if the first nominated sub-contractor withdraws; this means that delay in re-nominating is accountable to the employer. But the second point made in this case was that the delay *caused by the actual fact of withdrawal* of the nominated sub-contractor falls on the *contractor*, and may render him liable to damages if it causes a delay in the overall completion of the project. Even a clause providing for extension of time for delay on the part of a nominated sub-contractor will not avail the main contractor here, since the complete withdrawal of a sub-contractor (for example through insolvency) is not the same thing as a 'delay'. Nor can such delay by any stretch of the imagination be called *force majeure*.

The case which originally dealt with the question of the duty to nominate a new sub-contractor to replace the old was *Bickerton and Son Ltd* v *North West Metropolitan Regional Hospital Board* (1969). In this case nominated heating sub-contractors went into liquidation before starting work. It was held that under this particular form of contract, the employer had the duty to replace the nominated sub-contractor, and the main contractor was under no duty to find the replacement or to do the work himself. This is not necessarily the case with every form of contract, so each contract must be taken on its particular wording. Of course, no such problem arises if the sub-contractor is not nominated, since the duty to replace him lies with the main contractor, and the liability for the delay is with the main contractor.

Another example of the kind of case in which the delay in progress is wholly or partly attributable to the employer is where the employer has to provide some item under the contract, such as drawings or facilities or 'free-issue' goods or materials, and fails to do so properly or on time. If the employer's duty arises under the contract, then a failure will put the employer in breach of contract. As already stated, this will then set time at large and release any liquidated damages which might otherwise have been payable by the contractor for such delays as might be his own fault. The employer will wish for a power to set a fresh completion date, so as to be able to reactivate liquidated damages. This may be set out diagrammatically:

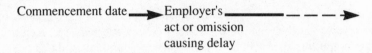

Commencement date ⟶ Employer's ⟶
act or omission
causing delay

Original	New
completion	completion
date is	date is
invalidated	set

Any
further
delays, if
by the
contractor,
will render
him liable
to liquidated
damages

But to achieve this, the employer requires an *express* power to extend the time for completion, and set a fresh completion date, either himself, or through his architect or engineer. This express power must *specifically* refer to the employer's act or omission or default. In the Canadian case of *Perini Pacific Ltd v Greater Vancouver Sewerage and Drainage District* (1966) the contract was for the construction of a sewage disposal plant. It had a clause in it allowing for an extension of time for 'extras, or delays occasioned by strikes, lockouts, force majeure or other cause beyond the control of the contractor'. This was held by the Court of Appeal of British Columbia to be inadequate to allow the employer to set a new completion date for his *own* acts or omissions: the words did not cover such acts or omissions in specific enough language. In this case the employer had delivered machinery, presumably on a 'free issue' basis, for the contract, and the machinery was in a defective state, and required repairs to be done to it. This was held to be a breach of contract by the employer, and it had the effect of invalidating the completion date. The work was completed ninety-nine days after the scheduled completion date, and the employer wished to extend the scheduled completion date by 46 days, and to recover liquidated damages of $53,000, at $1,000 per day for the other 53 days' delay, which, it was claimed, was accountable to the contractor. The Court held that *no* liquidated damages at all could be claimed here, since, having set time at large, and released liquidated damages, the employer could only claim liquidated damages if he had the power to set a new completion date, which, under the peculiar wording of this contract, the employer did not have.

CLAUSES DEALING WITH CLAIMS BY THE CONTRACTOR

Contractors who have suffered loss due to delay which is through no fault of their own will wish to know whether or not they are entitled to claim damages or additional payments under the contract. Not every loss due to delay will give the contractor the right to damages or to additional payments. One must look to the terms of the contract; one must also consider whether or not the employer is in breach of any of the terms of the contract.

The right to *damages* will arise if the employer is in breach of contract and if the breach causes loss or expense to the contractor. Even if no express provision is made for such a claim by the contractor, a breach by the employer of a term of the contract will, under ordinary principles of law, entitle the contractor to damages. Thus, for example, the JCT (1980) form of contract provides that the site will be handed over to the contractor on the Date of Possession. The Date of Possession is a date which should be entered in the Appendix. If possession of the site is not given to the contractor by the due date, the contractor may be legally entitled to repudiate the contract. But it is more probable that the contractor will wish to continue with the contract, and to claim extra payment by way of damages. This, he will be entitled to do, provided that he has actually suffered loss or damage due to the delay.

'The contract necessarily requires the building owner to give the contractor such possession, occupation or use as is necessary to enable him to perform the contract.'

(*London Borough of Hounslow* v *Twickenham Garden Developments Ltd* (1970).)

Express clauses entitling the contractor to extra payment on account of loss or expense

Here one must look at the precise form of contract that is being used. The JCT (1980), clause 26, for example, specifies seven matters which entitle the contractor to make a claim. These are: the contractor not having received in due time necessary instructions, drawings, details or levels from the architect for which he specifically applied in writing; the opening up for inspection of any work covered up; any discrepancy in or divergence between the contract drawings and/or the specification; the execution of work or supply of materials by the employer, or the failure by the employer to do these things if he has agreed to do so; the architect's instructions with regard to the postponement of any work to be executed under the contract; the failure of the employer to give in due time ingress to or egress from the site etc; the architect's instructions requiring a variation or in regard to the expenditure or provisional sums (except as provided).

The MF/1 1988 form of engineering contract also contains a number of clauses entitling the contractor to make claims for extra payment, as well as providing in clause 41 for a procedure for such claims.

'Direct loss and/or expense'

Damages are recoverable under the common law to the extent that they are compensation for such loss as the parties may reasonably foresee as a natural consequence of the breach of contract. The expression 'direct loss and/or expense', used in the JCT contract in the clause dealing with delays and claims probably covers the same heads of claim. The JCT (1980), clause 26.6 makes it clear that the common law rights of the contractor are preserved, by providing that the provisions of the clause are without prejudice to any other rights and remedies which the contractor may possess.

What heads of damages or loss are recoverable?

It is thought that in the absence of contractual provisions to the contrary the following heads of damages or loss are normally recoverable by the contractor in the circumstances discussed in the previous paragraphs.

1 Money paid by the contractor to other parties, such as sub-contractors, due to the delay: *Croudace Construction Ltd* v *Cawoods Concrete Products Ltd* (1978).
2 Wages and stores.
3 Accommodation, plant, tools, transport and storage.
4 Management costs and superintendence. But proper records are required to substantiate a claim. A claim based on a percentage of other items will be disallowed: *Tate and Lyle Food and Distribution Ltd* v *Greater London Council* (1982).
5 Increased costs.
6 Interest or financing charges.
7 Loss of productivity.
8 Loss of profit. *Wraight Ltd* v *P H and T (Holdings) Ltd* (1968). In this case, where work was suspended by the architect, and the contractors properly determined their employment under the JCT contract, it was held that loss of profit by the contractors was a direct and natural consequence of the determination of the contract, and the contractors were entitled to succeed in their claim.

10 Miscellaneous Obligations and Liabilities

In this final chapter we examine a number of instances where a party to a contract may incur a liability to another, or where persons who are not parties to the building or engineering contract may nevertheless undertake financial or other obligations in relation to the contract. We will be looking in particular at bonds and financial guarantees, indemnities, arbitration agreements, and at the limits of liability generally.

PERFORMANCE BONDS OR GUARANTEES

When a seller or contractor contracts to provide goods or work and materials or services, the buyer has the contractual benefit of the undertakings given by the seller or contractor, and may enforce those undertakings by legal action. Legal action is not always convenient for the buyer, and as we have seen, there are many instances where the buyer may take direct measures against the seller such as withholding payment or part of the payment, or such as taking *commercial* measures. However, these remedies may not offer the buyer sufficient security: the buyer may have made advance payments which he wishes to secure, or the buyer may have made complete payment, and may wish to secure the perform-ance of 'warranty' obligations by the seller after take-over; or the buyer may simply require additional security that the contract work will be performed properly and on time. 'Performance bonds', or guarantees, are ways of achieving these objectives by bringing another party in, who will provide financial guarantees for the buyer.

Any person may give a bond or guarantee to another person, but it is normally the practice in contracts of the kind we are considering for the buyer to require a bond or guarantee to be given by a bank, or by an insurance company, or by a parent company of the seller or contractor. It depends upon what is acceptable to the buyer. The word 'bond' is used in some contracts, and the word 'guarantee' is used in others. However, what is important is the form and wording of the undertaking rather than its description. The *function* of a bond may also lead parties to classify the bond as:

(a)   a bid bond or tender bond
(b)   an advance payment bond
(c)   a performance bond
(d)   a warranty bond.

But again, the expressions 'performance bond' or 'performance guarantee' or 'bank guarantee' may include any or all of the above, and it is important to examine the undertaking carefully to take note of its form and content and duration and to take note of the identity of the party giving the undertaking.

Objectives

Of the categories mentioned above, different objectives can be broadly discerned. The objective of the **bind bond** or **tender bond** is for the seller or contractor to furnish to the buyer a guarantee given by a third party that the third party will pay a sum of money to the buyer if the seller or contractor withdraws his tender within a stated period. The buyer gains from this the security of being able to allow himself the full period of time which he requires for consideration and appraisal of the tender. Tenders are offers, which are capable of being withdrawn at any time before acceptance. But the bid bond or tender bond, although for a relatively small percentage of the contract value, is a disincentive for the seller or contractor to withdraw his offer. A buyer who wishes the benefit of firm prices or the benefit of adequate time in which to consider the tender may therefore state that only those tenders which are accompanied by a bond in the required form will receive consideration.

Advance payment bonds are, as the name indicates, security for the buyer who makes advance, or stage payments. We saw in chapter 4 that a buyer who pays in advance does not necessarily acquire title to goods; nor has he any certainty, other than the reputation of his supplier, that the goods will be delivered on time or at all. This kind of bond will enable the buyer to claim a refund, to the amount guaranteed, if he does not receive the goods, or if the goods are not shipped in good order.

Performance bonds simply take this one stage further, since they not only secure advance payments, but may be used to secure the whole performance of the contract.

Warranty bonds are normally issued during the course of or at the completion of a contract, and are for smaller amounts, since by this time the customer will have paid for and received value under the contract, and will only be concerned to secure that the seller or contractor returns promptly to rectify defects, and that he maintains the necessary skills and equipment and spares on hand to do so. It will be noted that some of the things which a bond seeks to secure may be secured by 'retention money'. This is not surprising, since both of these things provide a financial 'hold' for the buyer over the seller, although the legal structure of each is different. There are no rules about whether the buyer or the seller will agree to arrange for bonds, or for retention money, or for both of these, or for neither of these, or for one in exchange for the other: it is a matter for commercial bargaining. Nor are there any rules, other than what is commercially acceptable, about the amounts or percentages of the price which are to be the subject of the bond or guarantee. If an advance payment is made, it will not necessarily be surprising to see that a bond for the full amount of the advance payment is required by the buyer. On the other hand ordinary performance bonds where stage payments are made for goods or value received will normally be for smaller percentages of the price.

The form of the bond

This will normally be dictated by the contract between the buyer and seller for the sale of goods or the purchase of building or engineering works. There will (in so far as bonds are required at all) be a clause stating what kinds of guarantees the seller is to give to the buyer, and when they are to be given, and whether the surety is to be a bank or insurance company or parent company of the seller, and for how long the guarantees are to last. The clause will often refer to an appendix of the contract which will contain a form which is to be the exact form of wording of the bond. The contract will also state which party is to bear the *cost* of obtaining the bond. These matters are all binding on both parties, so that utmost care is needed in studying and understanding the full implications of this part of the contract.

The legal implications of bonds and guarantees

It is important to understand the full legal implications of a bond. It sets up an agreement between the buyer, or the buyer's own bank, and the surety (ie the bank or other body giving the guarantee), and in many cases it stands completely independently of the main contract. It is usually stated to be irrevocable for a stated period of time. Although a bond is not identical to a letter of credit opened by a bank, the courts have often equated the position of a bank in the one case with its position in the other. In a number of cases, such as *Hamzeh Malas and Sons* v *British Imex Industries Ltd* (1958), involving an allegation by the customer that steel rods were not of the correct quality, and *Discount Records Ltd* v *Barclays Bank Ltd* (1975), involving a buyer who not only complained of the quality of goods received, but also who had in some cases received no goods at all, the courts have held that they will not stop payment on a letter of credit *unless a convincing case of fraud is made out.* An obligation about defective quality is no concern of the court. Even an allegation of fraud, short of substantial evidence, will not suffice. Similar principles apply in the case of bonds. In *Edward Owen Engineering Ltd* v *Barclays Bank International Ltd and Umma Bank* (1977), Lord DENNING stated:

> 'A performance bond is a new creature so far as we are concerned. It has many similarities to a letter of credit, with which of course we are very familiar. It has long been established that when a letter of credit is issued and confirmed by a bank, the bank must pay it if the documents are in order and the terms of the credit are satisfied. Any dispute between the buyer and the seller must be settled between themselves. The bank must honour the credit ... the performance guarantee stands on a similar footing to a letter of credit. The bank which gives a performance guarantee must honour that guarantee according to its terms. It is not concerned in the least with the relations between the supplier and the customer.'

However, it should be noted that Lord DENNING was speaking of the type of performance bond which is given in unqualified terms. Not all performance bonds are of this type, and there are forms of performance bond which require proof to the bank of a breach of contract by the seller, or verification of certain matters by the bank, before the bank is entitled to make payment on the bond. Some forms of performance bond require that the purchaser must show an arbitration award in his favour before payment can be made on the bond. These 'conditional' bonds are obviously more favourable to the seller, and present less of a risk for him, than the 'on demand', or 'on demand without proof or condition' forms of bond, which Lord DENNING was discussing. However, the latter form of bond is highly desirable for the customer because it is so easily enforceable, and not unnaturally, many customers, particularly those overseas, will insist on a bond in this form.

In *Edward Owen Engineering Ltd* v *Barclays Bank International Ltd and Umma Bank* (1977), a contract had been made between the English company, Edward Owen Engineering Ltd, and Libyan customers, for the supply of glasshouses. Payment was to be by an irrevocable, confirmed letter of credit. The Libyans had required a performance bond, payable on demand without proof or condition. This was issued by the Umma Bank to the Libyan customer, and Barclays Bank International Ltd guaranteed payment to the Umma Bank:

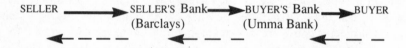

(The unbroken arrows represent the undertakings or guarantees entered into. The broken arrows represent the possible claims that may be made.)

In the event, Edward Owen Engineering Ltd was not satisfied with the letter of credit, since it was not confirmed. The company therefore repudiated its contract, and the Libyan customers then claimed on the performance bond. The Umma Bank then claimed on its guarantee given by Barclays Bank International Ltd. Edward Owen Engineering Ltd sought an injunction to stop Barclays from paying on the performance bond. This was refused by the High Court and Court of Appeal, which held that the bank was not concerned with the rights and wrongs of the dispute between the seller and the customer, but must simply pay on demand, without proof or condition. The only remedy for the seller was to sue the customer for damages (which might well have been a fruitless action in the circumstances!).

Such is the reality of performance bonds. The one exception to the absolute nature of an on demand bond is a clear case of fraud. However, no case of fraud was established in the above case, and as it will be very difficult to establish, the seller should only enter into a performance bond on the assumption that it *will*, in the great majority of cases, be enforceable.

Howe Richardson Scale Co Ltd v *Polimex Cekop and National Westminster Bank Ltd* (1977) is another example of this. In this case the Court of Appeal also refused an injunction to prevent the bank from paying on a performance bond, a refund of £25,000 which had originally been paid to the seller as an advance payment. Again, the bond was payable 'on first demand'; again, the similarity to a letter of credit was noted by the court.

In both cases, the problem for the English sellers was that, in consideration of the procuring of the bond by the bank, they had to give *indemnities* to the bank. This, in effect, meant that if the bank paid on the bond, the liability to pay would be passed 'down the line' to the sellers. Again, there is little that a seller can do about this, since a bank is not likely to furnish a performance bond without some form of indemnity or counter-guarantee from the seller. The form of wording will usually read along these lines: 'in consideration of your procuring the guarantee in the terms of the copy attached hereto . . . we agree to keep you indemnified . . .'. The indemnity may also contain a clause stating that any payment made by the bank 'shall be binding on us and shall be accepted by us as conclusive evidence that the sum stated is properly due'.

Summary

1 A purchaser will, justifiably, seek maximum security, particularly for advance payments, but also for general performance.

2 However, a seller or contractor should try to avoid unnecessary risks, and should evaluate these carefully before agreeing to give a bond, and before committing himself as to its amount and form.

3 The risks illustrated by the *Edward Owen* case, can be cut down by wording the bond so that it is in conditional form rather than the more absolute 'on demand' form.

4 The 'parent' company form of bond is for these reasons becoming more popular, since it can be written in conditional form, and is cheaper to provide than the bond given by a bank. The customer should not overlook the possible commercial advantages of such a bond, since it could be used to ensure prompt and effective *performance*, rather than simple financial redress.

5 The amount and duration of the bond, and terms on which it is to be returned and cancelled are also a vital part of the issue, since a seller which might not be willing to give a bond for a large sum in absolute form might be more willing to give such a bond for a smaller sum.

LETTERS OF COMFORT

We have seen in the course of this work various references to letters of intent: documents which are usually intended to, and often do, fall short of creating contractual relationships. A 'letter of comfort', or 'comfort letter', is a different thing altogether, since it relates more closely to the securing of financial obligations rather than to the commencement of preparations on a project. However, a letter of comfort has in common with a letter of intent the fact that the test of its legal effect is the test of whether or not there can be said to have been an *intention to create legal relations*. This test is an objective one, to be judged from the behaviour of the parties, and the character of the letter itself.

A letter of comfort commonly arises in the context of a loan or other form of financial accommodation being made to a subsidiary company. The creditor may have asked the parent company of the debtor to provide a financial guarantee. The parent company may have been reluctant to do so, and may have offered a letter of comfort instead of a guarantee. The difference between a guarantee and a letter of comfort will be a matter of legal draftsmanship in conveying one's intentions. A guarantee is an undertaking to answer for the debt or default of another. Provided that it is in writing, it will be legally enforceable. A letter of comfort may, if so worded, amount to a guarantee, and be enforceable as such, but that is not usually the intention of the company providing it. More commonly, the parent company which provides a letter of comfort will draft a document in language which, while giving some assurance of 'comfort' to the creditor, will be so worded as *not* to create any legally binding obligation. Provided that no intention to create legal relations can be shown, this will leave the parent, or other company providing the letter of comfort free from liability (although the debtor company will of course remain liable for the debt).

In an important commercial case the principle of intention to create legal relations in relation to letters of comfort has recently been clarified. In the case of *Kleinwort Benson Ltd* v *Malaysian Mining Corporation Berhad* (1988), the Queen's Bench Division of the High Court held that a letter of comfort *can* have legal effect, and that where an agreement amounted to a commercial transaction there was a *presumption in favour of an intention to create legal relations*, and the onus of proof on the party asserting that there was no such intention was a heavy one. In this particular case, Malaysian Mining Corporation Berhad issued letters of comfort prior to loans amounting in total to £10 million made by Kleinwort Benson Ltd to MMC Metals Ltd, a wholly owned subsidiary of Malaysian Mining Corporation Berhad. In 1985, about one year after the loans had been made, MMC Metals Ltd ceased trading. Kleinwort Benson Ltd brought an action against Malaysian Mining Corporation Ltd for, among other things, *damages for breach of warranty*, alleging that the undertaking given in the letters of comfort was legally binding. The relevant passage read as follows:

> 'It is our policy to ensure that the business of MMC Metals Ltd is conducted in such a way that MMC Metals Ltd is at all times in a position to meet its liabilities to you under the above arrangements.'

The court held that this letter was intended to create legal relations, and judgment was given to Kleinwort Benson Ltd in the agreed sum of £10,004,499, together with interest of £2,257,824. **STOP PRESS**. This case was reversed on appeal in 1989. See note on page 167.

INDEMNITIES

The word 'indemnity' occurs frequently in building and engineering and other commercial contracts. An indemnity is an agreement by one person to make another person secure against loss. It may arise in connection with insurance, or in connection with financial obligations, as seen in the previous paragraphs, or it may be that one party to a commercial contract simply agrees to indemnify the other against losses, damage, expenses, claims, etc, arising from certain activities or breaches of his duties. Thus a customer of a bank, who undertakes to indemnify the bank against liability under a bond is undertaking to repay to the bank any sums which the bank has to pay to the holder of the bond. An insurance company agrees to *indemnify* the insured, under a contract of insurance (other than life insurance or sickness or accident insurance). Thus the owner of a property who insures it against fire will receive an indemnity from the insurance company if the property is damaged by fire. This principle of indemnity means that the insured cannot make a profit out of the insurance policy, but will only receive the amount of his loss. (However, he can receive *less* than the amount of his loss if he insures the property for less than its full value.)

In building and engineering and other types of commercial contract, the reason why indemnities are sought by one party and given by the other is that there may be matters which give rise to claims by third parties. These may arise in connection with personal injuries to workmen and other third parties, or in connection with other property such as adjoining property, or in connection with intellectual property, which might be the cause of a complaint by a third party. Thus, for example, a person who designs an item to be made by another engineering company might be required to give an indemnity to that engineering company in the event of the item infringing the intellectual property rights of a third party, or in the event of it being the subject of any such claim. It is common for building and construction contracts to contain (a) provisions about insurance responsibilities; (b) provisions placing responsibilities for safety, and for the protection and care of the works and of materials, on one or the other of the parties; and (c) provisions about one party being under an obligation to indemnify the other for loss or damage or expense due to certain causes. These indemnity clauses are construed *strictly* by the courts, and an indemnity will be held to cover only those circumstances which it expressly or impliedly states to be covered. Two points are particularly worth noting:

1 If 'A' undertakes to indemnify 'B' against loss, this indemnity will normally be interpreted so as *not* to impose an indemnity in cases where the loss to 'B' is either wholly or partially caused by the *negligence of 'B'*. This principle is illustrated by the case of *Walters* v *Whessoe Ltd and Shell Refining Co Ltd* (1960), in which a labourer in the employment of

147

MISCELLANEOUS OBLIGATIONS AND LIABILITIES

Whessoe Ltd was killed by the lid of a petrol drum flying through the air, after an explosion, which had been caused by a combination of electric welding and explosive vapour. Both defendants were held to be partly to blame for the accident, in the ratio of 20% to Whessoe Ltd, and 80% to Shell. Shell then claimed to be entitled to indemnity from Whessoe Ltd, which was working on site as contractor for the putting up of a storage tank for Shell. It was held by the court that Shell was not entitled to an indemnity in these circumstances, since, although there was a clause in the contract under which the contractor agreed to indemnify the employer against all claims arising out of the operations, the clause would not be construed so as to impose an indemnity in circumstances where the employer's own negligence was one of the causes of the accident. This decision was followed in *AMF International Ltd* v *Magnet Bowling Ltd and GP Trentham Co Ltd* (1968), in which the employer (Magnet) and the main contractor (Trentham) were both held to be liable to a supplier of materials (AMF) on account of damage to the materials in a heavy storm. The employer then sought an indemnity from the main contractor under the main contract, which contained an indemnity clause. It was held that the clause was not operative in these circumstances, since the employer had also been negligent, and the clause would be construed as not being intended to operate where the employer had been negligent. (The employer did, however, recover from the main contractor on other grounds.)

2   The above case also raises a second point about indemnities; this is that an insurer who indemnifies the insured has the right to any remedy which the insured party would have had against the person who caused the loss or damage. Thus, where 'B' damages the property of 'A', and 'A' recovers an indemnity from the insurer, the insurer may claim the same remedy against 'B' that 'A' could have claimed:

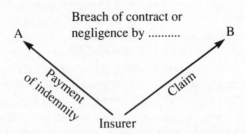

This right of the insurer is known as *subrogation*. It was relevant to the case of *AMF International Ltd* v *Magnet Bowling Ltd and G P Trentham Co Ltd*, because the property of AMF was insured by AMF. However, only the interest of AMF was covered by its insurance policy. This meant that when the property was damaged, due to its being inadequately protected against flood water, the employer and the main contractor could *not* rely upon the insurance policy, because far from protecting the employer and the main contractor, it conferred upon the insurance company a right of subrogation, so that the insurance company could recover from the employer and the main contractor any damages which the insured party, AMF could recover, for breach of contract or for negligence, on the part of the employer and the main contractor, in failing to protect the materials adequately. It follows that because one party to a contract may be liable to the other, or may have agreed to indemnify the other, the insurance policy should not be taken out in the name of one party only. If it is, it may be worthless in certain circumstances, because of the ability of the insurer, under the laws of subrogation, to recover its money from the party giving the indemnity, or responsible for the loss. A policy in the joint names of the parties will give greater protection, since the basic rule is that subrogation cannot be obtained against one of the parties to joint insurance.

THE DURATION OF LIABILITY

In this work we have discussed liability arising under contract, which will include guarantees and indemnities. We have also discussed other forms of liability which are relevant to building and engineering and other commercial contracts, such as liability in tort, in particular, the tort of negligence, and liability under statute, such as 'product liability' under the Consumer Protection Act 1987. We must now consider the duration of liability: liability does not last forever, and limits have been imposed upon its duration by statute.

The way in which the Limitation Act 1980 (which is the current statute setting time limits on liability) works is that it states that certain types of legal action must be commenced within specific periods of time. By 'commenced', it is meant that the official level commencement of proceedings, such as taking out a writ, or summons, or giving of notice of arbitration, must take place within the prescribed time limits.

The Limitation Act 1980 has, for our purposes, a number of different provisions about what the time limits are, depending upon the subject matter upon which the action is founded.

Actions founded on simple contract
Such actions may not be brought after the expiration of six years from the date on which the cause of action accrued.

Actions founded on a specialty
Such actions may not be brought after the expiration of twelve years from the date on which the cause of action accrued.

The difference between a *simple contract*, and a *specialty*, is that the specialty is made under *seal*. The twelve year period, as compared with the usual six year period, is one of the main reasons why purchasers will sometimes wish to make contracts under seal (see chapter 1 of this work). All contracts that are not specialties are classed as 'simple' contracts.

Actions founded on tort
Such actions may not be brought after the expiration of six years'from the date on which the cause of action accrued.

We have already discussed the difference between contract and tort earlier in this work. The most likely forms of tort to occur in relation to building and engineering contracts are *negligence*, *nuisance* (eg excessive noise or pollution), *Occupier's Liability* (ie liability for dangerous premises), *trespass* (such as wrongful refusal to return the property of another person), and *breach of statutory duty*. It should be noted that if the damages claimed in tort are for personal injuries, the time limit is reduced to three years, although the three year period can be extended for cases where the injuries only become evident after a period of time.

The 'cause of action': from when does time start to run?

This has long been a source of problems in commercial law. In contract, it is generally the date on which a *breach of contract* occurred. If payment is due on a specific date, and is not made, the cause of action will arise on that date, and time will start to run against the creditor. As regards *debts*, a right of action is capable of being *revived* by written acknowledgment of the debt, by the debtor or his agent to the creditor or his agent. It can also be revived by part payment of the debt, provided that the part payment is definitely referable to the contract.

As regards breaches of other obligations under contracts, the cause of action arises as soon as a breach occurs, but sometimes one can rely on the *last* breach as the date from which time begins to run. So, for example, if defective work is done during the course of a construction contract, the employer can rely on the *completion date* as the date from which time begins to run, since the breach is a continuing one, which continues up to the date of completion. This principle would not apply unless the breaches were of a continuing nature, so, for example, where separate deliveries of goods are concerned, one must take each delivery on its merits.

As far as *tort* is concerned there are a number of possible meanings given to the expression 'cause of action' depending upon the type of tort. In general, where fraud is not involved, the rule is that time begins to run *from when the damage is suffered*. This was decided after much deliberation by the House of Lords in the case of *Pirelli General Cable Works Ltd* v *Oscar Faber and Partners* (1982). This case illustrates the difficulties inherent in deciding when time begins to run. From a practical point of view it also highlights the importance of inspection of works, so that claims can be brought while it is still possible to do so. In this case, Oscar Faber and Partners, a firm of consulting engineers, were engaged by Pirelli General Cable Works Ltd to advise in relation to the building of works which included a chimney 48.8 m high. The work was designed and supplied by a nominated sub-contractor, which was in liquidation by the time of the claim. Because of a choice of unsuitable materials (lytag) used for the refractory inner lining of the chimney, cracks developed and eventually the chimney had to be partly demolished and replaced. Before considering the problem placed before the courts, we must ask why the action was brought against the consulting engineers rather than the other parties involved in the project.

Normally an employer will claim against his **main contractor** in these circumstances, since he has a contract with the main contractor. But a claim under a contract must be brought within six years of the completion of the work, unless the contract is under seal, in which case the relevant period will be twelve years. As we shall see shortly this was a simple contract, and the six year period had expired. Of course, a claim for *negligence* could be considered, but this can only be brought against a party who can be shown to be negligent, and as the main contractor had no responsibility for the design, negligence could not be alleged against the main contractor. Negligence might have been alleged against the nominated sub-contractor, but as the sub-contractor was in liquidation, such an action would have been pointless. So the claim was made, in negligence, against the consulting engineers. (Originally it was for breach of contract and negligence, however, by the time the claim reached the House of Lords, it was accepted that the claim for breach of contract was time barred.)

The sequence of events was as follows:

The engagement of the engineers was in March 1969.

The chimney was built in June and July 1969.

The evidence was that the cracks first appeared in April 1970.

The discovery of the cracks was in November 1977.

The writ was issued in October 1978.

If the action against the consulting engineers for breach of contract were to have succeeded, it would have had to have been brought by July 1975. As the action was brought for *negligence*, Pirelli argued that in negligence the 'cause of action' should date from when one should reasonably have been expected to have discovered the defect in the work. The evidence indicated that this would have been around the end of 1972, and if this argument had been accepted, this would have meant that the writ issued in October 1978 would have been just in time. But the House of Lords held that in cases of negligence of this kind, the six year period runs from the date when the damage actually occurs, and not from the date when it is or ought to have been discovered. Thus the six years had run from April 1970, and the claim brought by Pirelli was out of time.

This, then, is the basic law with regard to torts which do not involve fraud or death or personal injuries. However, to understand the law fully, several further points must be made.

1 Pirelli need not have been without a remedy, since a contract made under seal would have been enforceable for up to twelve years. For major projects, employers should give this matter serious consideration.

2 Pirelli lost the case on the technical point of time limits. It must always be remembered, however, that the burden of proof in negligence is a heavy one, and even if Pirelli had been within the time limits, it would still have had to prove the negligence of the defendants.

151

3   The *Pirelli* case decides that the cause of action accrues, and time starts to run, when physical damage occurs. It is, however, still a matter of serious contention what this actually means. In the later case of *Dove* v *Banhams Patent Locks Ltd* (1983), this point was illustrated. In this case an action for negligence was brought against burglary prevention specialists. They had installed a security gate at the basement entrance to a dwelling house owned by a person whom we may call 'Z'. 'Z' then sold the house to Dove.

The installation was in 1967.

The sale of the house to Dove was in 1976.

The security gate failed in 1979, when it was broken down by a burglar. Dove issued a writ in 1980, claiming damages for negligence resulting in the loss of Dove's property. The judge followed the *Pirelli* decision, ruling that time runs from when the damage occurs. In this case, however, the judge held that the damage occurred not when the defective work was completed, but when the gate was broken down by the burglar in 1979. Thus the action had been brought in time.

4   The period for which a seller may bear liability under a contract may be cut down by the terms of the contract. But the terms must satisfy the requirements of the Unfair Contract Terms Act.

5   Since the *Pirelli* case, there have been statutory changes in the law. One of these changes is in the *Latent Damage Act* 1986. This Act applies to cases of negligence causing damage (other than personal injuries), *where the damage is latent*. This was, of course, the problem in the *Pirelli* case, although the Act did not affect the result of that case. Under this new Act, the statutory time limit runs either from when the damage occurred, as before, *or, for another three years from when the injured party had the relevant knowledge of the material facts about the damage*. This Act came into force in 1986, and affects any relevant case which was not already statute barred before the new Act came into force. Although it mitigates the hardship of cases such as the *Pirelli* case, by allowing an extra three years from when the plaintiff ought to have known of the damage, liability does not run indefinitely, since the Act contains an *overall time limit of fifteen years* from the date of the act which is alleged to constitute negligence.

6   *Product liability*, under the Consumer Protection Act 1987, is treated as a form of tort. The time limit which applies is the *three year* time limit, which is the equivalent of the same time limit in ordinary cases of personal injuries caused by negligence. But the Act also contains an overall limit of *ten years*, dating from 'the relevant time'. The 'relevant time' means either the time when electricity was generated, or the time when any other product was supplied by the producer, 'importer' or 'own-brander' of the product, if that person is being sued; or, if the person being sued is not the producer, 'importer' or 'own-brander' (eg a mere supplier), then the relevant time is the time when the product was *last* supplied by a producer, 'importer' or 'own-brander'. Presumably, if a person is injured or suffers damage to property, and if it is too late to bring an action under the Consumer

Protection Act, because of the ten year time limit, this need not necessarily preclude him from bringing an action for *negligence*, where there may be an extension of time either for personal injuries or for latent damage to property. But of course the burden of proof is greater in an action for negligence.

<u>PERIODS OF LIMITATION</u>
(not including personal injuries
or Product Liability)

The 'cause of action'

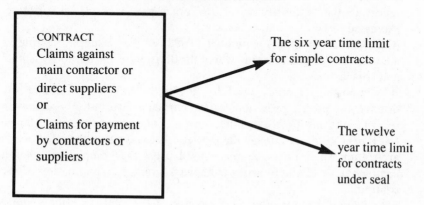

The 'cause of action'
ie the damage

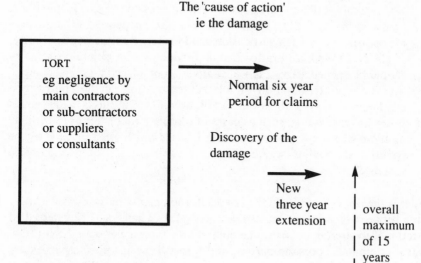

Arbitration provisions

The subject matter of the previous pages brings us to the question of arbitration provisions. They exist in most building and engineering contracts.

There is, however, no rule that a contract must contain an arbitration clause,

153

and many companies prefer to avoid arbitration, and to settle problems by other means. A few points about arbitration follow:

(i) An arbitrator may have a very wide jurisdiction, given by the terms of the contract. Thus power to arbitrate on any 'question, dispute or difference' arising between the employer and the contractor, will probably include issues relating to values, certificates, quality of work, causes of delays, extensions of time, variations, what is included in the contract, etc.

(ii) But the contract *may* expressly exclude (or simply not include) certain matters. Thus GC Works 1 provides for arbitration for disputes, differences or questions '*other* than a matter or thing arising out of or relating to Condition 51 (Fair Wages) or as to which the decision or report of the Authority or of any other person is by the Contract expressed to be final and conclusive'.

(GC Works 1 contains a number of clauses, for example relating to admission of people to a site, where the decision of the authority is final and conclusive.)

(iii) It is important to study carefully (preferably well in advance of any dispute) the precise provisions of the particular arbitration clause with regard to the *time* for the commencement of any arbitration proceedings. *GC Works* states that unless the parties otherwise agree, the reference to arbitration shall not take place until after the completion, alleged completion or abandonment of the works, or the determination of the contract.

Model Form A: states that performance of the contract *shall continue* during arbitration proceedings unless the engineer shall order the suspension thereof, or of any part thereof . . . (and goes on to provide that if any such suspension shall be ordered the reasonable expenses of the contractor occasioned by such suspension shall be added to the contract price.

The JCT (1980) arbitration clause provides that in general arbitration should be opened after practical completion or alleged practical completion, or after termination or alleged termination of the contractor's employment or after abandonment of the works. But this is made subject to several exceptions, such as cases of dispute about extensions of time, or about whether or not an instruction is one which is empowered by the conditions, or about whether or not a certificate has been improperly withheld.

What is the objective of including an arbitration clause in the contract? Any dispute between two parties may (unless excluded by contract) be referred to arbitration if the parties so wish. The point of including a clause in the contract is that it is binding upon the parties, and this will mean that the parties are *required* to submit the dispute which may later arise between them to arbitration, unless they *both* agree otherwise. It also means that the parties can, and usually do, state in the contract *who* is (or are) to be the arbitrator(s), or how such a person or persons are to be chosen. Furthermore, as already seen, the parties can, by choosing the wording of the arbitration clause carefully, retain a certain amount of control over the timing of the arbitration, and the question of whether or not a matter should first be referred to some other person, such as the architect or engineer, before the parties are allowed to submit it to arbitration. A written agreement to submit a dispute or difference to arbitration is binding on the parties to the agreement, and is subject to the Arbitration Acts of 1950 and 1979. It is not necessary to name the arbitrator at this stage: an agreement to submit the issue to three arbitrators, one to be chosen by each party, and the third (an umpire) to be chosen by the two arbitrators, is legally effective, although it is probably more common in institutional contracts to find that the provision is for only one arbitrator, to be chosen by the President for the time being of the particular institution named in the contract.

Why arbitration?

Arbitration is the referral of an issue, or dispute or difference between the parties to an arbitrator. The arbitrator is not a judge of a court, but is a person over whose selection the parties can (by the wording of the agreement) exert a certain amount of control. This means that they can, if they wish, ensure that a case is heard by an expert in the field, which, in technical cases could be a valuable way of saving time and costs. Furthermore, arbitrations are held in private, and companies which have no desire to air their disputes in public will find this beneficial. The rules of evidence are less formal than those of a court. It is also true, on occasions, that arbitration can be cheaper than legal action in a court.

Having said this, enthusiasm about arbitration needs to be tempered by one or two observations: it is not always cheap or quick: the arbitrator who has the ability of high court judges in sifting evidence will necessarily be rare. Furthermore, the parties may, by virtue of their agreement to refer a dispute to a specific kind of arbitration, incur travel and accommodation costs, as well as the cost of arbitrators' fees and arbitration premises. This will be particularly true of international arbitrations. Then, there is the question of the quality of the award: judges in courts tend to give judgment for or against a party, with compromise confined to a few well-known instances such as contributory negligence, whereas arbitrators in some fields have a reputation for compromise or 'splitting down the middle'. Privacy is perhaps the most valid reason for preferring arbitration to litigation. However, this too cannot be guaranteed in United Kingdom arbitrations, because in United Kingdom Arbitrations the Arbitration Act 1979 applies, and the arbitration may be the subject of an appeal to the courts on a point of law. Even before 1979, 'appeals' by way of 'stating a case' were permitted, although in rather more limited circumstances. The consequence of an appeal to a court is that the decision of the court on the point of law will be given in public, and reported just in the same way as any other court decision. International arbitrations, including those international arbitrations which are conducted in England, may be made to be final and conclusive and without appeal, if the parties so agree.

Glossary of Terms

The following guide may be found useful in understanding the meaning of terms commonly found in commercial, building, and engineering contracts.

Acceptance This expression takes its meaning from its context. It may mean the acceptance of an offer, ie the formation of a contract. It may mean something falling short of a contract, if the 'acceptance' is qualified. It can also mean acceptance of goods or services under a contract.

Acknowledgment This may amount to a mere confirmation that something has been received. Or it may amount to an acceptance of an offer. It could vary the offer, so as to be a counter-offer.

Administrator An official appointed by a court under an Administration Order made under the Insolvency Act 1986.

Advance Payment Bond A bond or guarantee given to secure the advance payment(s) made by a buyer.

Arbitration A form of adjudication of disputes or differences between parties to a contract or arbitration agreement. An arbitration agreement is an agreement to submit disputes or differences or questions arising between the parties to a person or to persons other than a court of law.

Bid Bond A bond provided at the time of the making of a bid or tender, usually as security that the bid or tender will not be withdrawn.

Charge A form of security created by a company in favour of another person. The charge confers rights over the charged assets of the company: 'fixed charge', or 'floating charge'.

Condition A major term of a contract.

Consequential Loss This expression has no accurate meaning unless it is defined in a contract. However, it is often understood to mean loss which does not flow directly and naturally from a breach of contract, but which arises as a secondary consequence of a breach of contract.

Entire Contract One in which complete performance by one party is a condition precedent to the liability of the other party to pay. In most cases the correct test of complete performance is 'substantial performance'.

Guarantee An undertaking made by one person to answer for the debt or default of another person. Must be evidenced in writing: Statute of Frauds 1677.

Indemnity An undertaking made by one person to keep another person free from loss.

Instruction to Proceed A request or instruction made by one person to another, requiring the delivery of goods or performance of services. This may have legal consequences, either as a contract (see chapter 1, offer and

156

acceptance), or, if falling short of the requirements of a contract, on the basis of 'quantum meruit'.

Letter of Comfort   Letter issued, for example, by parent company of debtor company, and intended to facilitate loan by creditor to debtor company, but intended to fall short of guarantee or other legal undertaking. Construction of letter of comfort is dependent upon wording and presumed intention of parties: not necessarily devoid of legal effect. See chapter 10.

Letter of Intent   Letter conveying a commercial decision to proceed with a transaction, but usually falling short of an offer or acceptance.

Lien   Legal right, arising in certain circumstances, to retain certain goods which one has in one's possession.

Limitation   Period of; statute of; expression used to define time limit(s) within which a person may bring legal action against another.

Liquidated Damages   Definite and ascertained sum agreed upon, at the time that the contract is formed, as damages for certain breaches of the contract.

Lump Sum Contract   Contract to complete work for a lump sum, as opposed to a contract under which the price is to be arrived at by subsequent measurement of work and materials.

Penalty   Contractual provision attempting to impose penal consequencies upon party in breach of contract. Penalties are void under English law.

Performance Bond   Bond or guarantee given by a surety; undertaking to pay money on demand or subject to stated conditions as security for the performance of obligations under a contract.

Product Liability   Liability for injury or damage caused by defective products. Expression used in particular with reference to form of liability which arises irrespective of fault or of any contractual relationship. Arises in UK under Consumer Protection Act 1987.

Quantum meruit   Right to be paid a reasonable remuneration for work done or goods supplied. May exist where contract has not been formed, or where contract is void, or where contract has no sum stated as price, or as alternative remedy for breach by purchaser.

Repudiation of a Contract   Indication by a party to a contract of a definite intention no longer to be bound by the contract. May be inferred from conduct.

Rescission of a Contract   The legal termination of a contract, in accordance with the express or implied terms of the contract. May occur, for example, on grounds of breach of condition, or on grounds of misrepresentation of material facts prior to the making of the contract.

Sub-contractor   Normally used to mean contractor to a main contractor. The expression has a number of possible meanings and definitions and context should always be taken into account.

Subrogation   Right of insurer who pays insured to avail himself of any right or remedy which the insured may have against other persons in respect of the loss or damage in respect of which the payment was made.

Substantial Performance   Doctrine or test for determining what amounts to complete performance of an entire contract. Work is normally considered to be performed if it is substantially performed.

Supplier This expression depends upon definition and context. May be a seller of goods or a supplier under a contract of hire or of hire-purchase. Sometimes used to mean 'supply only', as compared with contractor providing services.

Term (of a contract) Contractual undertaking. May be classified as a condition or a warranty, or its classification may be indeterminate.

Tort Civil injury or wrong of a type recognised by law, and for which the law provides a remedy. Examples of torts are: defamation, negligence, nuisance, trespass, breach of statutory duty.

Variation Expression normally used to mean alteration to or addition to or omission of work to be done under a contract, in accordance with the terms of the contract.

Variation of Contract This differs from the above, in so far as it concerns alteration of the *terms* of an existing contract, rather than the work to be done under a contract. Variation of a contract can only be done by mutual agreement by the parties to the contract, and to be valid will have to be supported by fresh consideration.

Waiver Intimation by one party to a contract that he will give up a right under the contract. May be made expressly or by conduct. Does not require fresh consideration for its validity. Once a waiver is made, it cannot be withdrawn.

Warranty A term of a contract less serious than a condition, and not entitling the party to whom it is given to terminate the contract for breach of it. In *insurance* contracts, a warranty *is a serious term*, and the insurer's liability may be repudiated unless it is complied with. Thus in insurance contracts, warranties are *conditions*.

Table of Cases

Table of Statutes

(in chronological order)

Select Bibliography

Building Contract Casebook, Vincent Powell-Smith and Michael P Furmston, Granada 1984

Building and Engineering Contracts, Alfred A Hudson, ed N Duncan-Wallace, Sweet and Maxwell 1979

Commercial Law, Robert Lowe, Sweet and Maxwell 1983

Effective Retention of Title Clauses, John Parris, Collins 1986

Elements of Mercantile Law, T M Stevens and G J Borrie, Butterworth 1978

Law of Agency, G H L Fridman, Butterworth 1978

Law of Contract, G C Cheshire and C H S Fifoot, ed Michael P Furmston, Butterworth 1981

Law of Contract, G H Treitel, Stevens 1983

Payment Obligations in Commercial and Financial Transactions, R M Goode, Sweet and Maxwell 1983

Product Liability: New Law Under the Consumer Protection Act 1987, Rodney Nelson-Jones and Peter Stewart, Fourmat 1987

Sale of Goods, J P Benjamin, Sweet and Maxwell 1981

Sale of Goods, Sir Mackenzie D E S Chalmers, Butterworth 1981

Index

STOP PRESS

The decision of the High Court in *Kleinwort Benson Ltd* v *Malaysian Mining Corporation Berhad* (1988), cited on page 146, was reversed by the Court of Appeal in 1989. The reversal was on the ground that the particular letter had no contractual effect, being a statement of *present fact* and not a promise of future conduct. See (1989) 1WLR 379. The case raises important distinctions between statements which are legally binding and those which are not. It is not possible to discuss these distinctions here, but the report deals with them in detail.